Miracles
and
Mysteries
Witnessed
by Nurses

LOTUS
LIBRARY

MIRACLES AND MYSTERIES WITNESSED BY NURSES

First published in Great Britain in 2019 by Lotus Library

A CIP catalogue record for this book is available from the British Library.

ISBN 978-1-7331232-1-1

Managing Editor for Lotus Library: Julie Gale Watson
Developmental Editor: Jennifer Watson Ervedosa
Cover design and typesetting by www.clareconnieshepherd.com

Lotus Library is an imprint of Watson Caring Science Institute,
a 501C(3) international non-profit foundation.

Watson Caring Science Institute,
4450 Arapahoe Avenue Suite 100,
Boulder, CO 80303
USA

www.watsoncaringscience.org

LOTUS
LIBRARY

Watson Caring
Science Institute

EDITED BY

JEAN WATSON

Miracles and Mysteries Witnessed by Nurses

LOTUS
LIBRARY

Renee,

Over the past few years you have taken me under your wing & taught me so much. You were there for me during the hardest time of my life. Thank you for all of your support & guidance, it has & continues to make all the difference. I want you to know you make a difference for me! I hope no matter what happens you know you have touched my life & I hope you are always open to miracles!

EDITED BY
JEAN WATSON

Contributing Authors

Prologue to Miracles and Mysteries shared here

As you enter into this sacred space, and read these personal vignettes and stories of miracles and mysteries - experienced by nurses and colleagues, you may experience a sense of disbelief; yet they are true as experienced by the person and situation. Truth is in the eye of the beholder or the reader. Rather than labeling or trying to classify the different miracles and mysteries that follow, I have chosen to just name them as each author's miracle, without any interpretation. As Heidegger acknowledged, when something is expressed so deeply, truthfully, and soulfully, the miracles speak for themselves. There is nothing else to say, other than to invite you to read, appreciate, bow down, and relish the deliciousness of life's wondrous unknowns – that can only be considered a miracle.

And, after entering into this space, can you not help but believe in miracles? I hope you will allow yourself, to see, realize, and appreciate all the miracles in your life.

Jean Watson

Do YOU believe in Miracles?

Nurses Do.

What is a Miracle?

"What does a miracle mean?
Well, in my daily moments I see different kinds
of miracles.
When you just appear in front of a patient who
was expecting you ...
When you see a little smile in someone who is
losing his last battle.
These kinds of miracles happen all the time,
the problem is we are much too busy to really
see them ...
What we do, we give our best every moment, even
in the hardest moments… it's really a miracle.

So just feel the moment and let these miracles give
the harmony we need in our human being."

**Mónica García, RN, ICU Specialist MSN
Instituto Nacional de Cancerologia
Bogotá, Colombia, South America**

What is Mystery?

It lives in the sea or a tree as it grows.
You can hear it, if you listen, to the wind as it blows.
It's there in a river as it flows to the sea.
It's the sound in the soul of someone becoming free
And it lives in the laughter of children at play
And in the blazing sun that gives light to the day.
It moves the planets and all the stars that shine.
It's been the mover of mountains, since the beginning of time.

Oh, Mystery you are alive; I feel you all around.
You are the fire in my heart; you are the holy sound.
You are all of life; it is to you that I sing.
Grant that I may feel you, always in everything.

And it lives in the waves as they crash upon the beach.
I have seen it in the goals that we have tried to reach.
I feel it in the light and I know it means so much.
I know it in your smile, my love, when our hearts do touch.
But when I listen deep inside, I feel best of all.
Like a moon that's glowing white and I listen to your call.
And I know you will carry me, I feel like the tide
Rushing through the ocean, and my heart is open wide.
Oh, Mystery you are alive. I feel you all around.
You are the fire in my heart; you are the holy sound.
You are all of life; it is to you that I sing.

Jeremy Geffen, Physician, Oncologist,
Beloved human and Founding Board member,
Watson Caring Science Institute
Boulder, Colorado, USA
(deceased 2015)

"Does anyone have the foggiest idea what sort of power
we blithely invoke? Or, as I suspect, does no one believe a
word of it? ...
... It is madness to wear ladies' straw hats and velvet
hats to church; we should all be wearing crash helmets.
Ushers should issue life preservers and signal flares; they
should lash us to our pews. For the sleeping god may
wake someday and take offense, or the waking god may
draw us to where we can never return ..."

Annie Dillard, *Teaching a Stone to Talk*

Great thinkers and poets alike dwell in miracles and mysteries.
To prepare for the miraculous moments from nurses, crash helmets
are called for, and we need to be lashed to our pews. In this collected
work, nurses share the harrowing and sublime, as well as their
miraculous and mysterious experiences, personal and professional.
I think there is no question, we all want miracles in our lives,
whether we believe in miracles or not. Facing life/death human
experiences every day, nurses confront unexplained phenomena
of life experiences, which do not conform to common explanatory
scientific models. This collected work, which features the experiences
of nurses who answered a call to share their profound nursing
miracles and mysteries with us, provides a forum where miracles and
mysteries of life/death can be shared. It is therefore being created
as a forum to honor and highlight life/death "unknowns;" allowing
for the reality of miracles to come back into our life and world. This
is an invitation to develop a miracle *consciousness*, allowing miracles
to enter and be affirmed in our lifeworld. Miracles, as unexplained
mysteries and non-conventional experiences, may be held secretly, or
may be ignored or suppressed, as there is no common space to share
them due to our institutional standards, norms, and culture. Yet, at
some level most people believe in miracles, or at least have moments
where they have to surrender to that which cannot be grasped or
believed, but rather accepted as acts of grace. As one nurse wrote,
"... that as we are in the presence of the patients who entrust their

care to us, we may be knowingly or unknowingly entering very sacred spiritual space" (see Cynthia's Miracle).

The miracles here are sacred stories, honoring holiness of self, the knowns and unknowns which speak for themselves. This collection embraces the wonders of not- knowing, in life/death and beyond. As another nurse writes, "Always leave room for mystery. It is the stuff of life" (see Nancy Rayos' miracle). In this work we open to those experiences of what we know least, transcending logos, honoring pathos, beyond empirical logical explanations, dwelling in unknowns and in "not-knowing," while embracing an inner ethos of mystery and miracles, that surprise even the nurse and persons themselves.

To honor these existential phenomenological unknowns, is to allow for miracles and mystery; it is to reside side-by-side, physical with non-physical/metaphysical, honoring intuitive, psychic, other dimensions of reality, presence of "angels in our midst," revealing wondrous, unexplained, often mystical phenomena, attributed to humankind beliefs and practices, across time and space.

Miracles – Definitions:

Miracles elude definition. Just as art is viewed and determined by the "seeing" of each individual person, so too are miracles known only by the experiencing person/s own eyes and lifeworld.

However, from mainstream sources, and dictionary definitions:

> "... a *miracle* is an extremely outstanding or unusual event, thing or accomplishment ... "

Merriam Webster's definition of the word miracle is:

> "An event manifesting divine intervention, a wonderful occurrence."

A study from Pew shows that young adults, the
so-called millennial generation ... profess widespread belief in the
afterlife, in heaven and hell and in miracles
(Pew Forum on Religion, 2010)

A miracle, in the Bible, (the often hoped-for outcome of prayers)
is a phenomenon – supernatural act.

> *"A miracle is a phenomenon not explained by known laws of nature. Criteria for classifying an event as a miracle vary. Often a religious text, such as the Bible or Quran, states that a miracle occurred, and believers may accept this as a fact."*

> *"So, I tell you, whatever you ask for in prayer, believe that you have received it, and it will be yours."*

If one returns to Biblical times, the Bible inspires faith through
many miracles and prayers. There are universal prayers that span
the globe, that call upon unknowns; there are pleas for divine
intervention; a call for angels and mysteries beyond usual beliefs and
expectations. Indeed, there is now so much research on the role of
prayer that cannot be explained in conventional science, that prayer
has to be taken seriously as a healing act. Transcending definitions,
a Chief Medical Officer and heart surgeon colleague of mine in
Florida, confided that, "There is so much research on prayer, I
consider it unethical not to pray for my patients before I do heart
surgery." He goes on to say, "None of my patients have expressed
any concern; except one patient said: 'It did not matter to him,
but if it is important to you, as the surgeon, please pray.'" Indeed,
more mainstream medicine, through the original and continuing
scholarship of Dr. Larry Dossey's research, and scientific attention
to the power of prayers has led to the proclamation: "Prayer is good
medicine" (Dossey, 1997).

Pre-Christian scholars, such as St. Augustine, a Bishop,
philosopher, theologian and saint in the Catholic Church (354 – 430

CE-BC), proclaimed that there was only one miracle – Creation itself ... All miracles reflect the creative nature of God. His writings report numerous personal experiences, as witness to miracles of healing throughout all of his journeys. His writing continues to be studied to this day. However, our modern, logical, scientific, rational mind does not know what to make of miracles, whether in Biblical early pre-Christian times, whether through research, poetry, through great thinkers, through reports in local television and global news, and whether through contemporary, current lived experiences of everyday people, including nurses' stories of miracles. Nevertheless, people all over the world still report miracles, and still believe in miracles, defying scientific laws and explanations. National polls over the past decade report a large percentage of persons believing in miracles:

"Nine out of ten people believe in miracles";

"Nearly 80 percent of all Americans, in fact, say they believe in miracles."
(Christian Post)

However, in the outer world, any contemporary, modern miracle is attributed to some rational explanation. We seek explanations to explain things which are contrary to the laws of nature. However, there remain unknowns of universal divine laws, which may also flow in harmony with nature and natural processes, yet to be rationally explained.

At another level, perhaps it is not that miracles are contrary to laws of nature; it is rather, they are outside of what we know of nature. Our natural laws are those that affirm natural order and rational explanations; however, even if miracles are explained scientifically, the wonder, awe, mystery and miraculous, disappear from our lifeworld, diminishing the hope and possibility of anything divine outside the human mind.

Poetry goes beyond, yet finds the divine in the natural order of things. For example, Emily Dickinson evoked reverie and ecstasy in the midst of clover and bees.

She invited us beyond logic, into transcendence within nature and natural laws.

TO make a prairie it takes a clover and one bee,

One clover, and a bee,
And revery.
The revery alone will do,
If bees are few.

Emily Dickinson

Ken Wilber, a world renowned scholar in the philosophy of science, has explored poetic contemplative questions and experiences outside scientific explanations. He highlighted and revealed that all contemplative traditions aim at going within and beyond reason per se. (Wilber, 2000: 271, in Watson, 2018: 62). As he has noted "no-knowing," a form of knowing, is explored personally to affirm higher domains of awareness – directly embrace experiences such as love ... This higher-level domain – ways of knowing/not knowing/experiencing – is based on hundreds of years of experimental introspection by sages and yogis with communal verification (Watson, 2018: 62).

So, what about Metaphysics, Miracles and Mysteries – the Existential – Spiritual: the 10th Caritas Process?

This book is a collection of nurses' stories, related to **Caritas 10 of the Ten Caritas Processes® of Watson's Theory of Transpersonal Caring**: (**www.watsoncaringscience.org**). All ten of the Caritas processes (conveying love, compassion, wisdom and caring) describe universal essentials of human caring, of which nurses encounter daily, but often these are not acknowledged, and may remain hidden from sharing, due to the professional scientific, objectified culture of institutional hospitals and technical-oriented empirical medicine.

The Tenth Caritas Process:

Opening to existential, spiritual, mystery, unknowns – Allowing for miracles. (Watson, 2008, 2018).

In my 2008 book, *Nursing: The Philosophy & Science of Caring,* I explained what I meant by this Caritas Process. I acknowledged that sometimes this one caring process is the most difficult to grasp.

"All I am trying to say is that our rational minds and modern science do not have all the answers to life and death and all the human conditions we face. We have to be open to unknowns we cannot control, even allowing for what we may consider a 'miracle' to enter our life and work. This process also acknowledges that the subjective world of the inner life experiences of self and other is ultimately a phenomenon, an ineffable mystery, affected by many, many factors that can never be fully explained. "... we ultimately dwell in mystery; life is not a problem to be solved, but a mystery to be lived. Human problems reside in ambiguity, paradox, and impermanence; suffering, healing, miraculous cures, synchronicity are all part of the dynamics of vibrating possibilities in our evolved consciousness ... the caritas conscious nurse 'allows for a miracle'; holds the patient's hope and faith for a miracle ... is open to unknowns, happenings at a higher order, even in the midst of modern precision medical science and concrete treatment. Thus ... always open to the mystery of a deeper order of the universe unfolding within a bigger picture than the human mind ... can hold."

(Watson, 2008 191-192).

Unitary Caring as Sacred Science –
Inviting Miracles

I have contexted this "invitation to miracles" collection within the evolving worldview of Unitary Caring Science, and Caring Science as Sacred Science (Watson, 2018, 2005; Watson and Smith, 2002). This framework of unitary "miracle-consciousness," invites the sacred, spirit, and mystery back into our lifeworld and work. The very notion of "unitary," from early 1970s work on unitary human beings, acknowledged the irreducible, indivisible, pan dimensionality of humans. Pan-dimensionality, and even trans-dimensionality of energy, are noted as non-linear without spatial or temporal attributes; wave patterns that continuously change from lower to higher frequency waves (Rogers' early 1970s work on unitary human beings).

The nature of transpersonal caring theory, unitary caring, and sacred science highlight premises, such as:

- a given moment transcends time, space, and physicality;
- consciousness is energy manifesting high frequency energy waves;
- human experiences are both immanent and transcendent – open and continuous with the evolving unitary consciousness of the universe.

In this evolved view, unitary thinking is a way of "experiencing the infinite" (Smith, 1999). "Experiencing the infinity" is revealed in these miracle stories and moments of nurses. In the stories, there is a perception of transcendence of the physical and material world; an expansion of time and space; honoring an unfolding and enfolding of mystery, spiritual connectedness, altered states of being, mystical wonders, other dimensions of realities, and Divine Love. (Smith, 2010; Watson, 1988, 2018).

This unitary metaphysical lens is less arrogant, less pious and more approachable, more authentic (Lather, 2017); it reveals spirit-filled experiences with the divine in many forms, where millions of persons around the world dwell and still have faith and believe. Lather proposed we ask new questions about our real world: What would practices look like, that were a response to the call of the holy other? This work honors and affirms: *Whatever anyone experiences is its own truth.* As Heidegger indicated soulful stories speak for themselves.

Miracles and mysteries transcend rational knowledge, thought patterns, usual mindsets, and "making sense." Nevertheless, millions of people around the globe have experienced what they call mysteries, miracles and unexplained phenomena. Likewise, non-Western cultures seem to acknowledge miracles more freely. For example, in my experience in India, Philippines, South America, and Africa miracles are quite normal. In Mexico and other Spanish-speaking countries, there is an openness and celebration of miracles in their everyday lifeworld of life and death. At a recent conference I attended along with 500 nurses in Mexico, I asked all who had experienced a miracle to raise their hand. Overwhelmingly almost every nurse in the audience raised their hand. However, our institutions and conventional scientific worldviews do not leave space for metaphysical, mystical concepts that nurses experience. For example, phenomena such as non-local consciousness, energy, soul, altered consciousness, coincidences, mystical-psychic phenomena, supernatural, angelic presence, apparitions, ghosts, non-rationality, spirit guides, and so on.

10 CARITAS PROCESSES ®

1. Sustaining humanistic-altruistic values by practice of loving–kindness, compassion and equanimity with self/others.

2. Being authentically present, enabling faith/hope/belief system; honoring subjective inner, life-world of self/others.

3. Being sensitive to self and others by cultivating own spiritual practices; beyond ego-self to transpersonal presence.

4. Developing and sustaining loving, trusting-caring relationships.

5. Allowing for expression of positive and negative feelings - authentically listening to another person's story.

6. Creatively problem-solving, 'solution-seeking' through caring process; full use of self and artistry of caring-healing practices via use of all ways of knowing/being/doing/becoming.

7. Engaging in transpersonal teaching and learning within context of caring relationship; staying within others' frame of reference-shift toward coaching model for expanded health/wellness.

8. Creating a healing environment at all levels; subtle environment for energetic authentic caring presence.

9. Reverentially assisting with basic needs as sacred acts, touching mindbodyspirit of others; sustaining human dignity.

10. Opening to spiritual, mystery, unknowns – allowing for miracles.

Angels

ANGELS You might see an angel anytime and anywhere.
Of course you have to open your eyes to a kind of
Second level, but it's not really hard. The whole business of
what's reality and what isn't has never been solved,
and probably never will be. So I don't care to
be too definite about anything….

Mary Oliver
Blue Horses; Poems
(https://www.goodreads.com/work/quotes/40167110)

So, "if and when we are ready, then we are free to embrace ANGELS, along with a new view of science, of our world, our universe. We realize we can re-enchant, re-spirit our world; we can sacramentalize each moment, even in the midst of profane, materialistic, corporate cultures. We then practice gratitude for each gift of life – we embrace beauty, truth, honesty, creativity, poetry, music, literature, drama and art … we wake up and enter … the human spirit, the heart and soul of our, and poet, Mary Oliver's, 'one precious life'"

(Watson, 2018: 58, 59).

From this conscious awakening we may need new sunglasses and crash helmets to "see" anew, to prepare for the miracles, mystery, unknowns, paradoxes, angels, ambiguities, mysticism, prayer, faith, trust, gratitude, blessings, and soul that nurses witness and share here.

I tell you the truth. If you have faith as small as a mustard seed, and you say to this mountain "Move from here to there" and it will move. Nothing will be impossible for you.

Mark 17: 20.

Closing:

In this collected work, nurses join saints and yogis, poets, artists, and inspired writers across time, by offering stories and vignettes of their personal experiences of mystery/miracles. Nurses, in particular, are witnesses to and experience multiple miracles in their midst, in small and grand ways; miracles that are unimageable or unexplainable. Miracles occur, in ways that do not conform to our usual experiences, and that open our hearts and minds to ponder angels, divine intervention, mystics, and unknowns. This nursing collection in-spirits, re-inspires, and re-enchants our world of healthcare, uniting us through our shared beliefs of humankind.

It is here perhaps, where we are all invited to enter the thin veil between here and there, and bow in revery to that which engages each of us into a divine and miraculous universe. In the words of poets and scientists alike, in this work, we validate Walt Whitman "as for me everything is a miracle" and Einstein "… live your life as though nothing is a miracle or as though everything is a miracle. A little knowledge is a dangerous thing. So is a lot." The remaining rhetorical questions – after reading these metaphysical – mysterious, miraculous stories and moments of nurses:

IS **Do YOU believe in miracles?**

Can you believe in these miracles as witnessed and reported by nurses?

Can you find miracles in your midst, whether you believe or not?

REFERENCES

February 2nd 2018: Christian Post: Retrieved from:
   https://www.christianpost.com/news/
   survey-9-in-10-americans-believe-in-miracles.html)

Dickinson. Emily (1924). A clover and a bee. In *The complete poems of Emily Dickinson.* Boston, MA: Little, Brown.

Dillard, Annie (1982). *Teaching a stone to talk: Expeditions and encounters.* New York: Harper & Row, pp. 40 – 41.

Dossey, L. (1997). *Prayer is good medicine.* San Francisco: Harper.

Lather, P. (2017). *(Post) critical methodologies: The science possible after the critique. The selected works of Patti Lather.* New York: Routledge.

Mark 11:24. *King James Bible.*

Oliver, Mary (2009). *Mysteries yes. Evidence: Poems by Mary Oliver.* Boston, MA: Beacon Press.

Pew Forum on Religion (2010). Retrieved from: (https://www.npr.org/templates/story/story.php?storyId=124007551)

Rogers, M. E. (1970). *An introduction to the theoretical basis of nursing*. Philadelphia, PA: FA Davis.

Smith, M. C. (2010). Nursing and Discipline of Nursing. In M. C. Smith and M. E. Parker (Eds), *Nursing theory and nursing practice*. Philadelphia, PA: FA Davis.

Watson, J. (2005). *Caring Science as sacred science*. Philadelphia, PA: FA Davis.

Watson, J. (2008). *Nursing: The philosophy and science of caring*. (Rev. edn.) Boulder, CO: University Press of Colorado.

Watson, J. (2018). *Unitary caring science: The philosophy and praxis of nursing*. Louisville, CO: University Press of Colorado.

Watson, J., Smith, M. C. (2002). Caring science and the science of unitary human beings: A trans-theoretical discourse for nursing knowledge development. *Journal of Advanced Nursing*. 37(5), 452- 461.

Wilber, K. (2000) in Watson, J. (2018). *Unitary caring science*. Louisville, CO: University Press of Colorado, p. 62.

Section I

Gloria's Miracles

Gloria Littlemouse RN, MSN, Ed. HTP, Caritas Coach,
Rossmoor, California, USA

Gloria's Miracle 1:

The special process of being open to mysteries and allowing miracles to enter my life came to me through my Native American grandmother. Because I believed in her and knew her own unique powers of intuition and divine trust, I found my first steps on the sacred path of helping others on their life's journey. I understood early on in my career as an End-of-Life nurse that spiritual needs had to be heard. Why? It is because I remember so vividly how afraid I was to discuss my own unusual near-death experiences. Learning to be aware of others fears and coaching myself to be present and available to those who were approaching the end of their journeys, gave me the ability to sit and listen with a complete sense of understanding. When patients have told me that I will never believe what they have been through, most often, I say, smiling, "I bet I will." That is because I know that I was saved twice from precarious circumstances in order to help those who have been placed in my path. And because I have experienced unconditional heart-centered spiritual healing, it is easy for me to truly love my profession and be passionate about Caring Science, and what it offers to those in times of need.

But the road to this place of continuous miracles all around me had not been such an easy one to travel. One early morning as a young child, I remember experiencing an excruciating pain in my neck. It was so stiff and I felt so weak. I was not sure what was happening; however, my father was a police officer, and I remember him putting me in the back of the squad car from the pediatrician's office and driving me with sirens to the hospital. I remember being poked in my back with this long needle and being told I could not move and would have to lay flat for 10 hours or I could end up paralyzed. I was so scared and I did not feel safe. My father had to work so he was hardly there as well as my mother. My grandmother would be at my side more than others; however, she had to take care of my younger brother who was at home with a broken arm. In this huge hospital I remember feeling alone. When people came into my room they were all covered with a mask, gown, and gloves. I was on the oncology floor and 30 years ago there was no hospice or palliative care. I was in the "terminal" area, which nobody wanted us children to know, but we all did. I had a friend who later became my roommate who died of end-stage renal disease and the boy next door died of leukemia, and so the story began.

Diagnosed with pneumococcal spinal meningitis, days turned into weeks, which was so agonizing. I am told I was in a coma for a week. When I woke up I remember I was so weak I could barely move. I do remember one nurse who had this beautiful smile. I really appreciated her because she was so kind. There were some nurses I did not care for and I was glad when they were off duty. I asked if my nurse could come back and she was with me a very long time and I remember hugging her goodbye when I was finally discharged.

I received several spinal tabs, which were painful, and I remember having to lay flat for hours after. Every time I would lay flat for hours, I would imagine myself being set free like a butterfly. When I was finally off isolation, the boy next door would come visit me every day. He once drew me a butterfly and told me that I would one day be free and fly away. I told him that I knew because I asked my doctor if I was going to die and he said, "Yes, there was a chance I might." I was never afraid of death and knew that my journey although short, seemed as if it was not quite ending. A few weeks later I got deathly ill, my white count went up and I was no longer able to walk. I remember having projectile vomiting and one morning when I opened my eyes there was a picture of a man with a beard and a brown cape. He looked like a monk. The picture said he was Padre Pio of Pietrelcina, Italy. He apparently was a priest who was involved in miracles if you said this prayer on the card. Later I would find out it was called a Novena. That afternoon, I was vomiting so badly I honesty had wished it just be over, because I could not tolerate the pain any longer. I had been hospitalized over a month already and was just too tired. This afternoon was different. I was febrile, the worst I had ever felt. When I started vomiting again I screamed out, "Padre Pio, help me!" I swear to this day he was standing at my doorway. The next morning, I woke up afebrile, everything had passed, my labs started turning around, and everyone kept telling me I was going to make it.

Just who was this monk guy? I had no idea; but I know he came to visit me. I was finally discharged from the hospital and swore I would go to Italy someday to visit his tomb, which was apparently famous.

In 2012, I finally had the ability to tour Italy and I was able to visit San Giovanni Rotondo, where the body of Padre Pio rests. During this tour they told me he was a very famous saint known for curing children with meningitis. I literally sat down, I guess it's a good thing there was a chair there. The lady asked me if I was okay because I apparently went pale. She also told me that he was known for bi-location and the children often saw him (although he was always in Italy), he appeared elsewhere in spirit to bring comfort to children in need. I know that day there was some form of higher power in my room and that day a miracle occurred, and I was cured.

Was this a miracle? I believe it changed my life. To this day, I believe that I saw him in the doorway of my room, just as I believe in the lady with the blue mantle who brought me peace at the time of my car accident, just as I believe in the nurse with the kind smile who gave me a very good reason to want to become a nurse myself.

Gloria's Miracle 2:

In 1994, while on a nurse travel assignment in Tampa, Florida, I was driving across the bridge going to work, when I spotted a car headed toward me out of my left peripheral view. The vehicle hit me in front of the driver's side door, and my car went spinning across the highway. In the midst of this surreal experience, I remembered that I had thought about just such an experience as I entered the highway earlier. What would happen if I was ever in a severe motor vehicle accident? All of my family lived in California, no one had any idea I was headed to my job, I had no emergency contact information in my purse. When the car came to a skidding stop, the front passenger door flew open and the contents of my purse were all over the front seat even though I had placed my purse in the back seat. Everything turned numb and I could not feel my fingers as rescue workers placed me on a stretcher. Then I noticed one of the nurses I worked with leaning over me and saying, "Oh, my God, Gloria, is that you?" She had stopped because she saw the accident happen. Her comment freaked me out because I wondered how badly I was hurt, especially after I heard that the man who had hit me died at the scene.

In Neuro-ICU in a different hospital from the one where I worked, I kept replaying things in my head. The life-flight team. The triage bay with so much blood. The trauma surgeon asking me who to call. They had found my pager on the street in pieces, but no next of kin information. The only number I could think of was that of my girlfriend so they called her to come. I kept asking if what was happening was real or a dream. Was I having a nightmare? Why had I thought about the accident before it happened?

The trauma surgeon informed me that I needed to give him consent to do surgery because he felt certain that I had internal bleeding. My body was black and blue from chin to abdomen with the bruising received when my chest hit the steering wheel and the windshield shattered. My seat belt and the car seat had both broken upon impact. All I remembered was that I had been lifted off my seat and a lady had come to tell me that I would be all right. The surgeon asked, "Was there someone else in the car with you?" I said, "No, but a lady who smelled like roses pulled me back down in my seat and covered me with a beautiful blue mantle with a lovely line of gold stars along the edges." She held me softly but tightly, saying, "Gloria, my daughter, do not worry, you will be in the hospital for a few days and then you will go home. I have so much work for you to do." Even though I have never been a religious person, I do not doubt the validity of a very spiritual presence coming to me in a time of need. I kept telling them about the lady who saved my life. I am still here and have almost died twice.

I heard the police officer telling the staff that it was a miracle that I was alive. He came to my bedside and asked me how fast I had been driving, and if I saw the car that hit me. When he walked away, he touched my arm and said, "Wow, you are a wonder!" I could hear the surgeon talking about spinal inflammation and the need for surgery. I said, "My arms and legs feel numb, but I do not need surgery." Still, he ordered me to have a CT scan and an MRI, and told the staff to prepare me for surgery. As I was wheeled into the operating room, the results came back: nothing was broken and there was no internal bleeding. Amazed, the surgeon touched my shoulder and said, "You have someone looking out for you."

By the next morning, I was up and moving about though I struggled to use my left arm. I asked if I could go home, as I had a dog locked up in my apartment that needed me. The surgeon said, "Absolutely not," and strongly suggested that I might need rehab for my left side. Luckily for me, my friend took my dog to her house, but I still wanted badly to get released and go home where I thought I would do better on my own. On the third day, I again asked if I might leave, but the surgeon again said, "No way," because my white blood cell count was over fifty and he added that I would not be allowed to leave the hospital until the WBC was twelve. He was not about to risk me having a blood clot with resulting complications. On the fourth day, I noticed that the phlebotomist walking in to draw my blood seemed to float above the floor. Her feet did not appear to touch the ground. I knew then that something miraculous was about to happen. I told her that I needed my white blood cell count to be twelve. She smiled and told me not to worry. She said, "I know you have a lot of work to do." It was exactly what the lady with the blue mantle had told me at the time of the car crash.

When the surgeon came in making his five o'clock in the evening rounds, I told him that I felt 100% certain that my WBC would be twelve and asked him to please sign my release papers. He said he was busy and he doubted that I was going to go anywhere anytime soon, but I insisted that he look more closely at my chart. I watched his face turn as white as his lab coat as he shook his head in disbelief. He told the nurse that I could be released the first thing in the morning, pausing in the doorway to say, "I wish you well. I know you are going to touch many lives."

Gloria Littlemouse

Dianna's

Miracles

Dianna S. Trush RN, Caritas Coach, Williams Bay, Wisconsin, USA

Dianna's Miracle 1:

I have been blessed to be attuned with the grace of miracles around me. I will mention two of the most powerful ones: first in my family and second, one from work. In 1978 my sister delivered a premature baby girl that weighted 3.5 pounds. She was also born with a heart condition – Tetralogy of Fallot – which at that time the only treatment was a heart transplant. She was discharged home after her weight increased to four pounds, my sister developed postpartum depression, and my mom, together with my brothers and I, took care of my infant niece. We couldn't let her cry since she would turn blue. The doctors gave her several months of life and advised us not to get too attached to her.

One evening I took her to my grandmother's house. My grandmother was a very faithful and loving woman. When I brought my niece over, "Abuela" took her to her room, laid her in her bed, and then she knelt down and prayed. She asked the Lord to give her heart in exchange for the baby's heart so that she could live. Abuela died a week later of a heart attack and my niece was completely cured! The doctor couldn't believe that she was the same baby. Today my niece is forty years old with children of her own. I can feel the tender loving person that she is and I know grandma's heart lives on.

Dianna's Miracle 2:

Last year at work around 5:00 PM, the call light in room 154 started going on. The staff of five wondered what was going on since there was no one in that room, and all the staff were in the nursing station. One of the CNAs went to the room, turned the call light off and as she left the room the call light went back on.

I then went to the room and I could feel a sense of inner peace. I said a prayer; turned off the call light, but as I turned my back the call light went back on. I remembered that the night before the resident that was in this room had passed. I think he had some unanswered feelings.

We called the electrician: however, since it was a Saturday and off tour, we were told, it would have to wait till Monday. The call light continued to go on and off.

One of the staff knew a person that had the grace of discerning spirits and she called her. The person knew immediately what was going on; without receiving past information, she told us that the gentleman's spirit was still in the room and needed assistance to depart to the other life.

She told us that she would attempt to talk to him and help him. She began to narrate what was happening; she held his hands and they began to talk. He stated that he wasn't ready and that he had regrets of not seeing his son. His body was aging and fearful. As she talked to him, assuring him that he had been forgiven and that it was his time to start a new life, they started walking out of the room. He continued to transform himself into a younger man and he was dressed in his uniform. As they passed through the nursing station, all of us felt a cold but peaceful chill. She told us that he was thanking us for the care we gave him. They walked to the elevator and there they said their goodbyes as he ascended up in the sky.

The call light ceased to ring and the night turned out to be a joyous occasion for thanking God for the blessing of His presence and for the gift that we had just received. As we told some of our other coworkers about what had happened, they thought it was something evil that had occurred. Our Chaplin gave us his beautiful explanation that this was a sign of God's love.

I believe that some things happen for which there is no scientific explanation, and that there are loving forces that surround us, such as faith, hope, and love! They have journeyed with me my whole life and have guided me to where I am today. I want to be a witness of God's everlasting love to all those that I encounter, and being a part of Caritas Coaching can continue to guide me.

Dianna S. Trush

Rudolf's Miracles

Rudolf Cymorr Kirby P. Martinez PhD, MA, RN, Manila, Philippines

Rudolf's Miracle 1:

The Boy Who Lived

"Our rational minds and modern science do not have all the answers to life and death ..."

I remember one experience that for me reflects allowing for mysteries and miracles to happen. It was when I was working as a staff nurse in a government hospital catering to sick children. Our hospital was the end referral hospital for the capital city of our country, which means we are the go-to hospital for all complicated cases in our country. We had this one sick child, a 15 – year-old boy diagnosed with encephalitis (swelling of the brain). He was restless and agitated when we got him up to the point that at times, we needed to restrain him for his own safety. A few days later, this demeanor changed and from being combative, he became stuporous and day by day his condition worsened. After a week he lost consciousness and fell into a coma.

While all this is happening, the medical team is at a loss as to the cause of his health deterioration. What we know is that his brain is continuously swelling, what we don't know is what's causing it.

Everyday feels like a race against time trying to find the cause of his disease so that we can devise a plan to treat it in the earliest possible time. We have done multiple tests on the child, almost every day there are laboratory exams to be done, and tests to be sent out just to find out what is causing his illness. We got to the point that we were sending out specimens (blood, urine, cerebrospinal fluid) as far as other countries since some laboratory tests are not available in our country. All tests yield negative results, even those that we sent abroad turned out negative. We were at a loss. It was beyond trying to find a needle in a haystack, we do not even know what the "needle" was in the first place.

While all this is going on, we nurses were very helpful to the patient and to the family, always reminding them that the patient is still here, alive although not awake, aware although he seems not to be. Because we were treating the patient without knowing the cause of the illness, it seems for the family that the treatment is futile. There is a palpable feeling of morosity in the unit as the nurses know that the family is contemplating withdrawing life-sustaining support from the child and to just care for the child at home.

On one occasion when I was assigned as a night duty nurse for the child, I tried to explore their decision for withdrawing life-sustaining support to their child. As part of building rapport, I sat by the patient's bed and asked the mother to tell me the last story that her child had told her. She told me that before her child became ill, he was with his friend and had gone to a picnic on a river near their place.

A day after their picnic, there was pain in his ear and after another day, he became restless and the rest was history as reflected in his admission records. Out of curiosity, I asked the mother if she had tried to consult a traditional healer in their town since I am aware that their town is well known for mystical healing practices. She said she had not tried to consult one since they were busy with all the things that had happened to their child. I told her it won't hurt to give it a try, to somehow cover all possible bases. Days after our conversation, I learned from my co-staff that the family sought consultation from one traditional healer by sending the shirt their child was wearing when he was with his friend on their picnic on

the river. The healer told the parent that a river spirit may have
been the cause of their child's condition. According to the healer,
"the spirit whispered something in the child's ear." Interestingly, the
healer was not told of the picnic or any other things regarding the
child's condition nor his medical history. To appease the "spirit," the
family did a ritual in their home as instructed by the healer.

Three days after the ritual, the patient regained consciousness. A
day later he began talking, telling about his journey to an unknown
land, full of trees and unique creatures ...

Up until this moment, we have no idea what really happened, but
what we are sure of is that the child lived. In hindsight, if we had
given up hope early, or if we had not allowed for the possibility of
any mystery or miracle for this child, we could have
lost one precious life.

Rudolf's Miracle 2:

A Familiar Voice, a Promise Kept

"Can I ask you something?" Mark said as he browsed my
Nursing Drug Handbook while I reviewed for my case presentation
scheduled that afternoon, for a patient on a far-flung ward from
where I am now.

Mark was my first patient, the first that I had taken care of as
a sophomore student nurse starting his clinical rotation. For him,
I defied many of the unwritten rules of my clinical instructors, all
for the sake of making him as comfortable as possible. I crossed the
boundary of the sacred nurse-patient relationship, of maintaining
a strict separation of my life and his. He was my patient, I was
his student nurse. It was all that it was supposed to be. But then
again, the universe works in mysterious ways. He became more
than a patient for me; he became my friend and I his companion.
Our lives became an intricate pattern of an elaborate embroidery,
deeply intertwined with each other. I was there during the most
difficult moment of his hospital stay for his leukemia treatment, even

excusing myself from class just to be there when his IV was being inserted for his chemotherapy. I even became a secret blood donor when he needed one. I became part of his family. They confided in me problems unrevealed by the Nursing Assessment, those that only a family member would understand and appreciate. I was given the rare opportunity to help by knowing him first as a person. I became part of his world and he part of mine.

"Of course, anything you like," I replied as I slowly brought down the notes that I was reading, gently looking down at him resting on my lap as I sat on his bed. And as I looked at his young fragile body, I remembered how little by little, cancer and chemotherapy took its toll on him, how he told me one day that his hair was falling out, that he is losing his appetite, that he is getting weaker. It was too much for a child to bear. It was even harder for me to watch this unfold right before my very eyes knowing that my limited knowledge and experience cannot prevent this from happening.

"Is it painful to die?" He asked as he looked at me with his innocent eyes, seemingly probing for an honest answer. "Why do you ask?" I responded as fear, anxiety, and shock spiraled down inside of me, as if the moment I dreaded the most was becoming a reality. Deep down, I knew this was coming, but I blindly looked the other way, as if denial would do any good. I've read his chart, browsed through books and articles, I knew his time was coming to an end… I just wouldn't accept it.

"I overheard the doctors," he said as he turned his face away from me, gently adjusting it as he rested upon my lap. "They said I was not responding to the chemotherapy, that there was nothing more they could do ... I have seen Mama crying at night ..."

Then there was a deafening silence. "Maybe it's painful to die, but I don't care," he continued as I was left dumbstruck by his sheer honesty and his way of saying things in a matter-of-fact manner. "I was lonely before you came ... I just don't care what the future will bring ... All that changed when you came ... You were the brother that I never had ... Even if I am always in pain, you made it bearable ..."

I was speechless, as if this was all a nightmare ... Wishing hard that I would wake up sooner than later. I feel I was in a suspended reality during this time.

"Promise me one thing," he said as if knowing that I was still trapped into believing that everything was all but a dream. I merely nodded as I tried with all my might that was left, to fight back the tears from flowing. I have to be strong for him, or at least appear to be.

"Can you take care of other children like me when I am gone? I want them to experience having you as their brother ... I want them to be as lucky as I am," he said as he slowly gazed at me eye to eye, wanting to hear my sincere response. "Don't talk like that, everything will be fine, you're going home this afternoon," I lied as I prepared my things for duty, making sure that our eyes never met. "I will always be there for all my patients especially you ... See you later before you go."

Then, for no apparent reason, he suddenly embraced me ... gently whispering:

"Thank you ... I will never forget you." This was all that I needed to hear. I was not as powerful as I would wish and think I could be in fighting back those tears. Silence was upon us as I embraced him back, pledging to myself, "I will make your wish come true whatever it takes, I promise."

A week later, Mark died.

Years after, I finished my BSN and enrolled in an MA program that focuses on children and I worked as a pediatric nurse for a number of years. Today I am a PhD prepared faculty of a University whose research work and advocacy focuses on children, cancer and palliative care.

Even now, I still hear Mark's voice in my sleep every time I feel that I am losing interest in the things that I am doing, reminding me why I am here in the first place ... because I am still fulfilling my promise to my very first patient, Mark.

Rudolf Cymorr Kirby P. Martinez

Rosemary's Miracles

Rosemary T. Hoffmann RN, MSN, Caritas Coach,
Malverne, New York, USA

Rosemary's Miracle 1:

Miracles happen without a doubt. They occur when you are open to a higher spirit and the calling of an inner voice directing you. At least that is what happened when I answered yes.

The first miracle occurred one evening when I received a phone call from the adult daughter of a nurse with whom I had worked but had not seen for some time. She wanted to let me know that her mother was critically ill and not expected to live. Would I come to the hospital? I said of course.

Before leaving something told me to bring a green scapular, a religious object thought to bring healing to the sick. I searched and found one and placed it in my pocket. When I arrived at the hospital I saw my friend on a ventilator and unresponsive. Her husband and grown children were gathered at her bedside. The scapular was still in my pocket as I was not sure how her family would receive it. As I went out in the hallway her husband was there and crying. I told him of the scapular and asked if I could pin it to his wife's gown. He said it was fine and so I did.

I left the hospital praying for the intercession of the Blessed Mother to restore this mother to her family. Several days passed when I received word that she was much better. Eventually she made a full recovery and returned to her nursing profession. Surely this was a miracle of faith. To this day her family attributes it to the intercession of the Blessed Mother. I merely answered yes to the inner call to be the mediator.

Rosemary's Miracle 2:

The second miracle occurred one day at the hospital. A young Chinese girl was involved in a motorcycle accident and suffered a major traumatic brain injury. She was in a grave state and seemingly unaware. One of my colleagues approached me in the hallway and told me of a request by the girl's mother that a group of people of different faiths pray at her daughter's bedside. Again, I answered yes and set about assembling staff of different faiths and asked them to come with me to pray at the woman's bedside. Amazingly no one said no and as we entered the room we saw before us a young unresponsive woman. Her hands and legs were contracted and the thought surely was that there was little hope for her. I asked everyone to encircle the bed to pray for her in their own words.

As we prayed we all stared in amazement as her lips began to move, then her hands and feet. After leaving I told the charge nurse and called her Attending to inform them of what we had just witnessed. They did not seem impressed but rather spoke of the poor prognosis. Several days later her mother arrived from China and planned to transport her back home. I thought for sure that she went home to die or at best to live out her life in a nursing facility. How wrong I was.

Almost two years later she returned to the hospital to thank the staff that had cared for her. I was in disbelief but remembered again what we had seen before us. When we are open we will see. Miracles do happen when we listen for and to that inner call.

Rosemary T. Hoffmann

Nancy's Miracles

Nancy Rollins Gantz PhD, RN, MSN, MBA, BS,
Portland, Oregon, USA

Nancy's Miracle 1:

She was a first-year nursing student and recently assigned a clinical rotation on a medical-surgical floor. Jane had always wanted to be a nurse and Florence Nightingale was her idol. She was assigned an older lady, called "the crabby old lady" by staff, and who was to be discharged the next day to her nursing home. Miss Baker was not a positive or happy woman and it seemed no one could get along with her. After one shift Jane could see why people didn't want to be assigned to Miss Baker.

The first time Jane came into her room, Miss Baker asked her why she was so happy! In her opinion there wasn't anything to be happy about. Regardless of the examples Jane gave her for why we should be happy, Miss Baker wasn't buying any of it. After much conversation, Jane found out that the only thing that would make Miss Baker happy was to see the Portland Rose Gardens one last time before she died. Of course, Jane told her she had lots of years ahead of her, and opportunities to see the gardens again. Miss Baker grew angry and said, "You don't know what you're talking about!" She went on to tell Jane she had no family and hated where she lived as they didn't care about her.

Jane went on a quick break thinking about what she could do to brighten up Miss Baker's life. Jane went back into Miss Baker's room and said that she would take her up to the Rose Gardens in the morning, as it was her day off, being Saturday. Miss Baker's eyes grew big and she couldn't believe what she was hearing.

The next day Jane picked up Miss Baker, drove to the Rose Gardens and the sun was bright without a cloud in the sky. Miss Baker cried when she saw the roses, even though she tried so hard to be stoic and "tough." Jane took her back to the hospital and several hours later Miss Baker was transferred to the nursing home.

The following week the nursing home called to say that Miss Baker had passed away. They also questioned what happened at the hospital as when she returned to the nursing home she was a different person. Miss Baker smiled for the first time and was actually a happy person.

(The story does not end here ... for the student nurse was "strongly" spoken to, and told that doing something like that is totally unacceptable ... Personally, I know the nursing student would do the same thing again).

Nancy's Miracle 2:

The year was 1914 in a small town in southern Minnesota. A future pharmacist, Les, said to Mildred, ten years his junior, "Someday, I'm going to give you a diamond for those big, beautiful brown eyes!" When Mildred turned sixteen years old two years later she took the train from Elmore, Minnesota to Fort Lewis, Washington to see Les at the Army base but only with the promise to her mother that she would not get married. The day after she arrived, Les and Mildred were married.

It was a marriage that very few are fortunate and blessed to experience. Their two daughters and five grandchildren only observed a genuine and unconditional love between Les and Mildred. Never a harsh word was said to one another. Their friends were always in wonder how a marriage could be so endearing, caring, compassionate; and strong.

In 1963 Mildred became ill and later was diagnosed with stage 4 small colon cancer. She died over a period of three years, never lost her love for Les as he was also by her side through the difficult times. In September of 1966 Mildred lay semi-comatose in the hospital. She appeared to be restless and was calling out Les' name. Les came to see her, bent down and kissed her. Her eyes stopped rolling, her restlessness was gone, and she closed her eyes as she crossed into God's hands. She had been waiting for him to come and see her so she could peacefully leave.

Nancy Rollins Gantz

Stephanie and Matthew's Miracle

Stephanie Ahmed, Mother Lexington, Massachusetts, USA
Matthew R. Wilkie, Son Tewksbury, Massachusetts, USA

> *"Be patient toward all that is unsolved in your heart and try to love the questions themselves".*
> Rilke

The following vignette describes a miraculous exchange of perspectives between a mother and her son, Matthew, who is a person living with depression. Together, we hope that by sharing our story, someone who is silently living with the stigma of mental illness realizes that they do not walk alone.

Matthew (M): As a person with depression, I have struggled to understand the diagnosis, questioning: "Why – why do I have this? Will it ever get better? If events in my life were different, would the outcome and the diagnosis be the same?" and with consideration of life events, "I wonder which events even contributed to this? ... I had a happy childhood."

Stephanie (S): Parents of children with depression grapple with heartbreaking questions too. Thinking about my son, I remain unsure of the when, or the why. Moments of our lives play over and over in my mind. In my own quest to understand, I have struggled to pinpoint the onset: "When did it happen?" and, "Why did it happen? Why is he like this?" and of course, "Did I cause this?"

M: Between recognition of an existing problem, and the subsequent years it may take to achieve a diagnosis (and honestly, beyond), pain and suffering inevitably are encountered. Retrospectively, during adolescence, I now recognize the change I experienced, transforming from a happy and well-adjusted kid to someone who struggled with incredible sadness and lack of motivation. With the change and the etiology now obvious, I liken the impact of depression on my development, relationships, and experiences, to an invasive vine that chokes a blooming flower; depriving me of self-actualization – of that which could have been.

S: Bearing witness to a life which fails to unfold as promised, by the fairytales so often read to young children, is painful. For my bright and beautiful son, the journey was, and remains, hard and not infrequently; it impacts his relationships – ours included. Challenging interactions have been followed by the sharpness of his anger and lengthy periods of estrangement, during which my heart ceaselessly ached as I worried; would he be okay ... Where was he, was he safe tonight?

Throughout my career as a nurse practitioner, I have had the privilege of intersecting with countless numbers of patients during the most vulnerable moments of their lives, offering care and healing. Yet, as a mother, his mother, I was unable to "fix this." While alive, my son, as I knew him, died. When a person is diagnosed with cancer, everyone rallies around them, with love and support. When there is a death, there is a funeral or ritual ceremony, cards, flowers, and a public out-pouring of that love and support. With Matthew's depression and frequent estrangement, the hopes and dreams died. I carried the loss of him alone and most often, in silence. There were no flowers or cards for us. It was then that I recognized the ceaseless aching of my heart as grief.

M: Depression often contributes to insomnia and on one particularly wakeful night, as I made my way toward the kitchen, I saw my 86-year-old grandmother sitting on the living-room couch with rosary beads in hand, crying and praying to God. I remained out of sight but heard her speaking of my self-imposed estrangement from my mother. Despite an eighteen-month period without contact, I never stopped loving my mother. Witnessing my grandmother's pain and knowing the values she instilled in all of us, the importance of family, and the integrity of the family unit, enabled me to put my own pain aside and to reach out to my mother.

S: Rather unexpectedly, Matthew texted me and asked to speak with me; it was an olive branch of sorts. This was an opportunity to re-establish a connection, but memories of past interactions admittedly contributed to my trepidation. Arriving with conviction, in the middle of a snow storm so severe that the Governor had issued a travel ban, Matthew encountered me in the driveway. Taking the shovel from my hand, he completed the arduous task of snow removal. With the real work still ahead of us, we sat down to talk.

M: As we began, I admittedly was unsure whether the past could be hurdled, given previous discussions. However, for the first time, I felt that my mother not only listened but actually understood my version of events– and I hers. It was an incredibly validating feeling and an important stepping stone on our path to rebuilding the loving relationship we once had before the onset of this debilitating mental illness.

S: As a Caritas Coach, I called deeply on my own learning in Caring Science. I set an intention for a positive outcome. Seeking to communicate at a higher vibration than perhaps achieved during previous interactions, I received him with love – the highest source of healing (Watson, 2008). Matthew sat before me, for the first time, with an open stance, thoughtfully engaging, offering his thoughts and willingly listening to mine. Together, we retraced a history that whilst imperfect, was uniquely ours. Seeking to understand the perspective of the other, we revisited the questions, realizing that, in a sense, neither the questions nor the answers were important. Through acceptance and love, a painful history was miraculously transformed into one of connection, hope, and promise.

S: Recently, while attending a Caring Science conference, a nurse colleague who was leading the closing intention, invited participants to send a transformative text to a loved one. She said, "*Sometimes saying the words: I love you, thank you, please forgive me and I forgive you; can be so hard to say, but they are transformative.*" I knew in the moment, Matthew would be the recipient of my text. I said, "*Matthew, I love you, thank you, please forgive me and I forgive you. These are the hardest words to say ... We often miss the opportunities to say them and I want to say them to you* ♥ ." He responded within moments, texting, "*I love you too. Thanks for raising me well and sticking by me. I forgive you for any of the times I have felt upset or abandoned by you and (now) understand most of those times were my perception and not reality. Glad we are in the spot we have made it to, today. Looking forward to many more awesome years ahead.*"

Together: Today, taking counsel from Rilke, we agree that we will no longer revisit questions or seek the answers which cannot be given to us. Together, we will simply live them and continue loving each other, for that is the point and truly where miracles can be encountered.

Stephanie Ahmed and Matthew R. Wilkie

Watson, J. (2008). *Nursing: The philosophy and science of caring* (Rev. edn.). Boulder, CO: University Press of Colorado.

Emily's Miracle

Emily Barr CPNP, CNM, MSN, PhD student, Caritas Coach,
Denver, Colorado, USA

I want to share a short story with you. My brother was an
accomplished actor. I don't tell many people that, but it's part of
my story. In the spring of 2013, I was trying to reach him. He
lived in NYC with his wife and kids, and my oldest daughter was
a student in NYC at the time and she had been trying to see him
and wasn't able to connect, which was unusual. So, I was texting
and calling and leaving him messages. I then had a very vivid
dream. In the dream I was in his apartment in Manhattan (though
a dream version of this apartment) and in one room there was his
wife and kids and I couldn't find him. I started looking in all the
rooms and finally found him all alone in a large dark room, and he
wasn't well. He was very sad and alone and I couldn't connect with
him. I woke up and the next day I sent a message to a woman who
had been an assistant of his. I said, "Do you know where Phil is?
I have to tell you I had a dream, and I think something is wrong, I
can tell. We used to share a room growing up, and we would listen
to each other breathe at night. I know something is wrong." She
texted back that she wasn't sure where he was but that she thought
he was okay. (She did know exactly where he was, but couldn't
tell me at the time.) He was at a rehab. He had relapsed and had
started using substances after twenty-three years of being sober.
Tragically, he died less than a year later. This was my intuition, my
connection; the love I shared with him telling me there
was a problem.

As you will see, the *Gift of Intuition* is important for nursing care
(and life). My intuition told me that my brother needed help, and I

believe that most of us have not fully tapped into this spiritual gift that can provide healing, comfort, and guidance in our professional practices (and our lives).

Emily Barr

Grissel's Miracle

Grissel Hernandez RN, BSN, MPH, HNB-BC, Caritas Coach,
Stanford, California, USA

Facebook Posting

February 28, 2019 – included with permission

[I] woke up this morning asking God to send me angels to support me and while looking for some papers I have on the refrigerator this note flew out to the side. It was Mami's note on her last birthday card to me in 2017. You have no idea how much I need to hear this especially today. Miracles and angels abound just open your eyes and heart to them.

(I love you butterfly
May God always protect you)

Section II

Inova Nurses Miracles & Mysteries

Unfolding Mysteries within the Human Energy System.

About Inova Health System

Inova Health System is Northern Virginia's leading nonprofit healthcare provider, recognized in 2019 by U.S. News & World Report which named the Inova Fairfax Medical Campus the #1 hospital in the Washington, DC, region with four of Inova's five hospitals receiving five-star rankings from the Centers for Medicare and Medicaid Services. Our mission is to provide world-class healthcare – every time, every touch – to each person in every community we have the privilege to serve. Inova's 18,000 team members serve more than 2 million individuals annually through an integrated network of hospitals, primary and specialty care practices, emergency and urgent care centers, outpatient services and destination institutes.

These miracles and mysteries of Inova nurses we lovingly compiled by **Jennifer Drake DNP, RN, NPD-BC, ONC, Caritas Coach, Springfield Virginia USA**

Introduction

Mary Ann Friesen PHD, RN, CPHQ, Falls Church Virginia USA

Healing Touch is defined as "a relaxing, nurturing, heart-centered, biofield (energy) therapy. Gentle, intentional touch assists in balancing physical, mental, emotional and spiritual well-being. Healing Touch assists in creating a coherent and balanced energy field, supporting one's inherent ability to heal." (Anderson, Anselme & Hart, 2017, p. 10). There are five levels of training for Healing Touch. Healing Touch was introduced to the Inova Health System in 2012 and since then, over 660 nurses have been trained. Classes continue to be offered and five research studies have been conducted on the impact of Healing Touch on nurses and patients. Several exemplars provided by nurses at Inova illustrate miracles and mysteries they have experienced using Healing Touch.

Diane Miracle/Mystery 1

Diane Swengros MSN, RN, CHTP, Springfield, Virginia, USA

One day while I was a student studying Healing Touch, a colleague asked me to provide a session prior to her surgery. She had been fighting a battle with cancer and this time had to have abdominal surgery. As I worked on her energy system I had the intention of surrounding her with glorious white light, setting my intention for her greatest good. I became somewhat frustrated as the harder I tried to bathe her in white light, the light kept morphing into yellow light. I was perplexed. I concentrated harder and yet all that appeared was yellow. I had remembered what my instructor had taught us, that the energy would know what was needed and where to go. I moved to the allow mode and embraced the yellow light. My colleague drank it in, seeped in it, and radiated brilliant golden yellow light. The next morning, immediately prior to her surgery, a friend and fellow colleague, also a student of Healing Touch, met her at the hospital to provide another session. Later that day I saw my friend and asked her how her session went. She replied, "I have no idea, all I could see was this brilliant yellow light everywhere I worked." My colleague's surgery went well and she recovered smoothly. For those who may not know much about the chakra system, yellow is the color of the solar chakra, which sits right at the top of the abdominal region. To charge up and protect the area of her abdominal surgery it is logical that yellow light would be just what was needed. We strive so hard to be in the know; however, there is much to be learned in the mystery of it all.

Diane Swengros

Theresa Miracle/Mystery 2

Theresa Davis RN, NE-BC, CHTP, FAAN, Woodbridge, Virginia, USA
ICU Nurses Witness Healing Touch in Action

Our first Healing Touch study in critical care began an exciting journey of healing and growth for nurses and their patients. The research team collaborated with Healing Touch experts in the development of a Healing Touch intervention that was feasible to use in a research study within the critical care setting. A patient enrolled in the study was in respiratory distress, breathing rapidly at a rate of 32 per minute and was obviously uncomfortable. After introducing myself to him and his wife, I gently began the Healing Touch intervention. As I began the intervention, his respiratory rate slowed, his labored breathing abated, and he fell asleep. The heat I felt previously around his chest and abdomen became cool and smooth after the Healing Touch intervention. He was now peaceful and appeared comfortable. His wife sat quietly by the bedside. The monitor indicated his heart rate and his respiratory rate steadily decreased; he became calm and slept soundly for the first time since arriving in the ICU. In the Tele-ICU, nurses who participated in the study through virtual voice and video technology observed the phenomenon of the effects of Healing Touch over and over again, as we enrolled 87 patients across four hospitals. Our findings in this foundational research were significant for decreased heart rate and respiratory rate, increased O_2 saturation, and decreased pain and anxiety. We were witnesses to the wonder of many miracles throughout this study.

Theresa Davis

Liliana Miracle/Mystery 3

Liliana G. Suchicital BSN, RN, CBN, CHTP, ONC, Fairfax, Virginia, USA

Seeking and Finding the Healer Within

One snowy day, a colleague from work called me upset, seeking Healing Touch. Her husband was admitted to an ICU, on a ventilator, and was fighting it. She was terrified and wanted to help him relax and to let the machines help him to breathe.

When I arrived, I provided a Healing Touch to help her relax. As I entered her husband's room I found him fighting the ventilator with his eyes closed, his respirations were labored. All the alarms in the room were going off, lots of beeping. His heart rate was rapid; his BP was high and his respirations over 32. I began connecting his chakras and then worked on clearing his field. I did a pain drain, but mostly I worked to clear his lungs. I kept focusing on his breath. I told him, "Just breathe, just let it go. Do not fight the machines anymore. Relax and breathe."

I spent 40 minutes with him. This is a long time for Healing Touch, but I did not feel tired. I felt energized. When I finished, I held his feet and invited him to return. I noticed his blood pressure had lowered, his heart rate had lowered, and his respiratory rate was 26 and no longer labored, and alarms were no longer beeping.

As I held his feet, he opened his eyes for the first time. I went to get his wife, and he looked right at her. The next day, she texted me a photo of her husband, sitting in a chair, on nasal cannula oxygen, being shaved. She said, "Look what you did!" He was totally different. This experience helped me realize the tool that I have. We study and practice Healing Touch and the gift remains hidden until we explore the possibilities. I got the sense that I had what I needed within me to help and heal others. My thoughts changed this day. They say we are healers. I used to say, "No I am a nurse. I use science and medicine and technology ..." but this experience showed me that I am a healer. I thought that I used tools, and today I realized that I am the tool. If it hadn't snowed, and my plans weren't cancelled, I would not have been available to participate in this miracle.

Liliana G. Suchicital

Robin Miracle/Mystery 4

Robin R. Jackson MSN, RN-BC, CCRN, CCNS, CHTP, Alexandria, Virginia, USA

Healing and Comfort for My Son

My journey to becoming certified in Healing Touch (HT) took me down many roads in self-exploration and self-evaluation. I am always amazed and have learned to trust the feelings I have when doing HT. Those feelings lead me to help clients. I provided several sessions on my son, who is active duty military. He expressed skepticism about how HT works and wanted to know the science in HT.

The first session he reported pain in his knees, a sore throat and stress from the loss of a friend. I started the session looking at his whole energy field. He was very tense so I started with a Chakra Connection, to help him to relax. I then provided pain techniques for his knees and throat. The final technique I performed was a mind clearing technique to help promote relaxation. He did tell me he still had the knee pain, but later fell asleep for the night (and later told me he had not been able to sleep before the HT). I noticed the next day he was calmer and seemed happier.

A few months later, after he laid his motorcycle down on a winding mountain road, I provided another HT session for him. He had bruising and road rash. I could feel he was very tense. As I scanned down his energy field, I felt areas of hot and cold in patches, the cold areas were over the areas of the injuries. I again started with the Chakra Connection, followed by the mind clearing, but this time I was guided to add a technique of light sweeping motions along the meridians. I noticed while I was doing the session I felt calmer and I saw a green light. Green is associated with the Heart Chakra. While I was doing HT, I felt guided to stay a little longer in some areas such as his flank area. The temperature of his energy field was even throughout with the final scan, and he fell asleep while I was doing HT. Over several sessions, he stated that he was feeling better and sleeping better. He told me later he was able to rest and the injured areas were not sore. He actually seemed to enjoy HT and has asked me about doing a session since; not a bad way to convert a skeptic.

Robin R. Jackson

Val Miracle/Mystery 5

Val Lincoln PhD, RN, AHN-C, Lake Ann, Michigan, USA

It is true that seemingly unrelated moments or events, with a tincture of time and retrospection, may emerge into a pattern. Sometimes you will think: That was a seminal event, but you can't imagine the future influence or outcome. So many events of this nature have happened to me. An important mystery in my life had to do with a chance connection with internationally renowned physician and author Dr. Elizabeth Kubler Ross.

My professional nursing career began in the mid-1970s and primarily focused on all things Perinatal High Risk in nature. My first position was as a Maternal Child Health nurse (labor, delivery, post-partum & newborn nursery), and later I worked as a Neonatal Intensive Care nurse and a Perinatal Coordinator, to name a few. As a Regional Perinatal Coordinator at a perinatal center, one of my responsibilities was to facilitate a continuing education conference of interest to perinatal professionals. Elizabeth Kubler Ross had achieved worldwide acclaim for her seminal work on the journey of dying in her book *On Death and Dying* (1969) which brought the stages of dying to the larger cultural consciousness.

My mother-in-law had briefly met Dr. Kubler Ross and suggested she would be a great speaker as she had expanded her interests to the process of dying in children. She cautioned me, that Elizabeth was also interested in more "esoteric spiritual matters" as she put it, whispering aside that, "She talks about having Spiritual Guides of some sort ... and I hope for your sake she doesn't go off-topic from the more acceptable topic of supporting children through the dying process ... "

At the time, I was about six months pregnant with my son Nicolas and as circumstances would have it, I had multiple cardiac issues and problems. As we nurses would colloquially say, "You know being an NICU nurse is a distinct high risk OB factor, don't you?" To that end, I would wear the old-fashioned cardiac diagnostic monitors that gave the person a button to push to record their voice to describe what was going on if one felt an abnormal cardiac event. It is in this nexus of pregnancy that interesting moments came to me with a message.

The day of Dr. Ross' presentation was upon us, and there was a lot of stress swirling around. Several thousand folks wanted to attend her presentation. We made arrangements for televising her presentation into other venues from the very large host church building. The moment came when I took a few moments to meet with her personally, to get clear on my introductory remarks, and to ensure that she had everything she needed. As a very seasoned speaker she had absolutely no concerns, yet her eyebrow lifted in concern ... I am moderately tall and was seemingly very pregnant, compared to her remarkably petite stature. And then without any words, she approached me closer, placed both of her hands on my pregnant belly, closed her eyes as if to see and to hear something very distant. She very quietly, and with her pronounced Swiss accent, simply offered that, "Your baby boy will be just fine, and you will be just fine." My heart rate and rhythm immediately raced and bounced around. I remember pushing the recording button and said, "Well, if my recording is very abnormal, it is because a world-renowned physician who I never met before in my life just did a little séance with my belly and determined my boy and I will be fine." The thing is, I did not know the sex of my baby until his birth several months later. I pretty much swept this, shall we say unusual moment, under the carpet right away as I was still on pins and needles as to just "what" she would be saying in her presentation. Spirit Guides? Angels? But no, she stayed on the topic of supporting children in the dying process with the interpretations of their art and stories. I wondered what the person doing the Holter interpretation thought about my heart's dysrhythmia and my notation! My story ends. Or so I thought.

About twelve years later, Dr. Kubler Ross was speaking in the Detroit area and a few friends decided to join me in attending her presentation. Her focus at that time was about "taking care of the business of healing in your life." She gave a great presentation, and opened up the format to asking and receiving questions. A few questions in, she stood up and loudly asked, "Who in this auditorium

knows that they are not doing the work that they are called to do?"
No one was answering her. Hundreds of participants, and no one
was responding. Then in a sort of altered state, I could sense that
my right arm was either lifting up, or being lifted up. All I knew was
that I was not doing the lifting. Then the second mysterious moment
occurred. She stood up, all possibly five feet of her, and with
uncharacteristic volume in her voice, she shouted:

"YOU! YOU! I know you. You are NOT doing the work that you
are called to do. And you must. Do you even KNOW the work you
are to do? It is URGENT that you do whatever it takes, to do this
critical work. I don't care if you think you are busy, that you don't
have the time, that you don't have the money – whatever – if need
be, you should come live with me at my farm in Virginia (as memory
serves)."

The rest is a blur. Except the look on my friends' faces! And I
thought to myself, "What they don't know yet is that I DID NOT
lift my arm up ... And I also thought, I can't believe that in that
capacity-filled auditorium that I was the only one who was not doing
the work they were called to do. Problem was: I thought I WAS
doing the work I was called to do: leading a perinatal center. Trust
me, with wine and gab fest, that night was charged.

Several years pass. As life would have it, I would need to leave
the leadership role of the perinatal center as we faced an interstate
move. As Spirit would have it, I received an unsolicited *Journal of
Holistic Nursing* in the mail, and I discovered the Certificate Program
in Holistic Nursing. After completing the program, I was asked to
join the faculty to provide education about the newest subspecialty
in nursing. I thoroughly enjoyed the deep work and the great
relationships, etc. During this time, a friend of mine said, "There is a
great program you would probably love on holistic stuff" at my Alma
Mater. And so, my journey toward my dissertation on holistic nursing
began — by what I thought was — by accident.

As I faced the move to Minnesota, I thought, "What job do you
want to create for yourself? When were you the most personally
and professionally satisfied?" I answered an ad for a part-time
NICU nurse position at a brand-new hospital, Woodwinds Health

Campus. Within weeks of my orientation, however, I was involved in a challenging car accident, so I told my head nurse that I wasn't sure just when I could fulfill my obligations to the team. She asked if I would stay on, to maybe help her with some chart audits, etc. I accepted the invitation. The very first chart I reviewed, while looking for the anesthesia report, I discovered a Healing Touch documentation form. I thought to myself, I didn't even mention that I have training in Healing Touch and Reiki from the 1980s. Shortly thereafter, the position of Director of Integrative Services was offered to me, which has brought me the greatest personal and professional satisfaction of my lifetime for fourteen years now.

Sometimes a position that never existed before will appear before your eyes. Then, and only then do you connect the dots that someone like Dr. Elizabeth Kubler Ross presented to you, and you will pay attention to the unsolicited professional Journal that comes to your home address. Pay Attention. Do the preparation. Let the pattern emerge.

Val Lincoln

Healing Touch Reference

Anderson, J. G., Anselme, L. C. & Hart, L. K. (2017). *Foundations and practice of Healing Touch*. Lakewood, CO: Healing Beyond Borders.

Section III

Nancy's Miracle

Nancy L. Rayos RN, HN-BC, Warren, Michigan, USA

My son was born a 7 pound, 4 ounce full-term baby with
an APGAR score of 7, which quickly dropped to 1. He was
transported within twelve hours to C. S. Mott Children's Hospital
in Ann Arbor, Michigan, where he underwent an experimental
treatment to facilitate the exchange of oxygen and carbon dioxide
in his lungs. When he was eight days old, after no progress had
been made toward Michael being able to breathe on his own, his
NICU Intensivist tearfully told my husband and I that she had
been lying in bed at night, racking her brain to determine what was
wrong and why nothing was working for our boy. She told us that
while no one was giving up, that we would have to make difficult
decisions soon. Our son was on a ventilator, with 100% oxygen
keeping his saturation in the mid 80s. This was not compatible
with life.

On the one-hour drive home to our two older children, we had
time to discuss what we thought would be best. I felt deeply that it
would be wrong to continue to chemically sedate him, artificially
feed and breathe for him, and continue his life if all we were doing
was postponing the inevitable. I loved my boy, and wanted nothing
more than to take him home to his brother and sister and watch
him grow up, but I did not want to extend his life if it was not
meant to be. We decided that extubating Michael was the only
choice we had. Artificially extending his life was not an option
for us.

The next morning, the ventilation was removed for a routine
exchange of equipment. During the exchange, Michael began
breathing on his own. His oxygen saturation moved into the

90s and stayed there. This May, he graduates from Wayne State University with a Bachelor of Science degree in Psychology. Always leave room for mystery. It is the stuff of life.

Nancy L. Rayos

Cynthia's Miracle

Cynthia L. Holle DNP, MBA, RN, Salem, Connecticut, USA

When I was around seven, in the mid-1960s, my grandmother, who was in her early seventies, had an myocardial infraction. Care of those with cardiac emergencies was not as sophisticated then as it is now, and my grandfather was told that my grandmother had a 50/50 chance of surviving. My mother's cousin, who was a nurse at Yale where my grandmother was being cared for, told my mom that while that's what the physician told my grandfather, his real prognosis was far less optimistic.

We lived in a small town about half an hour away from Yale New Haven Hospital. My mom visited Nana in the hospital and was grief-stricken by her prognosis. When she left the hospital in the evening, instead of going straight home, she went to our small-town church. Christ Episcopal Church in Bethany in that era kept the front door unlocked for parishioners who felt the need to pray in the church. It was winter, dark, and cold. My mother went into the cold church and prayed for her mother. She prayed for her survival, and the intention of her prayer was that my grandmother's grandchildren would be blessed with the time to know her. My mom was her mother's last baby, an unexpected "change of life baby," and was around twenty-eight years old at the time. As a later-life baby, she did not know her own grandmother and she prayed for me, and for future grandchildren, to have that privilege. After praying a bit, my mom said she knew everything was going to be fine, that my grandmother would survive. She said the church was warm, and she felt a peace and knowledge of a prayer answered.

My grandmother did indeed survive. When she recovered and got stronger, my grandparents made the thirty-minute trip to spend an afternoon with us in Bethany. (This was usually a big trip for them. They lived in New Haven and "going out to the country" was considered far!) My mom said to my grandmother, "I have something to tell you about that evening I visited you." My grandmother responded, "I have something to tell you, too." My grandmother went first. My grandmother told my mother that about thirty minutes after my mom left, and for three days, every time she opened her eyes she saw Christ standing at the foot of her bed. She said she knew she was not going to die because he did not have his arms outstretched, beckoning her. His arms were at his side, and he was keeping watch over her. She described the landscape around him as being sandy and rocky, with scrub-brush type vegetation. She felt peaceful and safe.

My mom then told my grandmother about her experience in the church. By comparing stories, they realized that my grandmother's vision of Christ began about the same time my mother was praying in the church.

My grandmother's family left Germany and moved to the US when she was around thirteen years old. English was her second language and while she was proficient, her education stopped after high school. She was not a student of history, did not travel, and did not have knowledge of the landscape in Israel. I don't believe she conjured this image up from academic memories. She was, however, a person of incredibly strong faith, and helped nurture that gift in the rest of us.

One could call a prayer and a recovery coincidental. My grandmother may have recovered even if my mom didn't go to our church and pray for her. But we know the appearance of Christ happened about the same time that my mother entered our church and started praying. Each person (mother and grandmother) kept the events to themselves until that day many weeks later. My grandmother told her version first, and so was not subconsciously influenced by my mother's experience. I do not find this to be a coincidence. I do believe in miracles. I believe that my mother prayed an unselfish prayer and God answered that prayer. I do wonder if God uses miracles not just for the intended recipient, like my grandmother, but as proof for the rest of us of His care and love for us and that He does hear us. It's interesting to note that my grandmother is the person who encouraged me to become a nurse when I was a child. Her suggestion started me down a long path of caring for others!

My grandmother lived to her eighties, and she lived long enough to know that I graduated from nursing school. She knew, and was known, by all seven of her grandchildren. My mother received what she asked for.

My husband and our children recently spent Christmas in the Holy Land. On a trip between Jerusalem and Qumran, I gazed out the window and realized I was looking at terrain that was exactly as my grandmother described it. It was an amazing moment of connectedness for me.

I think there have been times in my nursing career when I've entered sacred space with my patients, when a patient in my care overcame incredibly bad odds or circumstances in order to survive or realize a strong desire or finish a task. I feel like in those instances I have been allowed the grace to be a small thread in the fabric of a miracle. Thank you for illuminating this aspect of nursing care. When we are in the presence of patients who entrust their care to us, we may be knowingly or unknowingly entering very sacred spiritual space.

Cynthia L. Holle

Gayle's Miracle

Gayle L. Casterline PhD, RN, AHN-BC, Boiling Springs,
North Carolina, USA

Sean was dying of Acquired Immunodeficiency Syndrome
(AIDS). I remember thinking on first glance that the bed looked
unusually large, but I soon realized that significant weight loss was
simply dwarfing the figure within it. His eyes were closed. He was
breathing quietly. I walked into the room and took a seat by the
head of his bed. I was managing a federally funded, multi-center,
longitudinal clinical trial examining the natural progression of
Human Immunodeficiency Virus (HIV) disease in men and boys
with hemophilia. This was the first time I had met Sean, although we
had spoken on the phone. I knew a lot about Sean from the research
team. The medical director had cared for him and his HIV disease
for ten years. Sean was bright and funny and motivated. Everybody
loved him and there was much sorrow in his imminent passing.

Sean opened his eyes and smiled at me. "Hi, Sean," I said. "I'm
the nurse from the research team. Do you remember speaking with
me the other day?"

Sean threw his head back and searched his mind for the answer.
"Yes," he said. "You told me you had just moved here
from California."

"That's right," I agreed. "Lucky for me, I get to work with
you now."

"Maybe not for long," Sean said quietly. "I'm dying, you know."

The flavor of his remark penetrated the air between us. He
searched my eyes for a response. I was hardly prepared for such a
frank discussion moments after walking through the door. I fixed my
gaze on his and asked, "How do you know?"

"I can just feel it," he answered.

"Are you uncomfortable?" I asked.

"Not really," he said. "Does my dying make you uncomfortable?"

Was he testing me, I thought. "Not really," I responded.

He smiled and closed his eyes to rest. Did I pass the test, I wondered? We sat quietly together for a few minutes. This was his second hospital admission this month. He had three active infections and took dozens of medications each day. He had lost thirty pounds over the last six months. I quickly scanned the room. It was full of life and love. There was a bouquet of flowers a bit past their prime, a half dozen cards pinned to the bulletin board, and a half-finished jigsaw puzzle on a card table. A get-well balloon hung inches from the floor, its helium nearly exhausted. A picture of Sean at the beach with two friends illustrated a more robust body and happier times. They had their arms around each other, standing in the water, laughing. Sean opened his eyes again.

I had to admit to myself that I had been a little afraid of what to expect on our first meeting. He looked thin and tired. There were dark circles under his eyes. His forearms were discolored from multiple blood draws.

"Are you up for a game of twenty questions?" I asked.

"Proceed," he joked back. Relieved, I pulled out the protocol book and went down the list of subjective questions. He answered each one slowly, thoughtfully.

"Do you think this study will help me?" Sean asked.

"No, Sean, I don't." I said truthfully.

"Do you think the study will help someone else like me?" he continued.

"I think the study will explain how real people like you are affected by the virus," I said. "Do you think that information will be helpful to someone else?"

"Yes," he said, offering his bruised arm. "You can take a blood sample now."

As I finished, Sean asked abruptly, "Do you believe in God?"

I turned to face him. "Yes, I do," I said.

"How do you know there's a God?" he asked.

I thought about his question for a moment. "Sometimes when I pray and I let myself be quiet enough, I can feel God's presence," I said. "And sometimes when I hear a bird sing, or watch the ocean waves roll in, or meet someone like you, I am comforted that God has an awesome plan for everything. Do you pray, Sean?"

"Sometimes," he said quietly.

"Would you like to pray right now?" I asked.

Sean lowered his eyes and nodded. I took his hands in my hands and we prayed together. We concluded with the Lord's Prayer, which Sean repeated effortlessly.

"Thank you," he whispered as I prepared to leave. "Let's pray again sometime."

"I'll keep you in my prayers, Sean." I assured him.

Sean died the next day. He was only twelve years old.

Gayle L. Casterline

JoAnne's

Miracle

JoAnne Auger RN, CHPPN, Caritas Coach,
San Diego, California, USA

Walking on Holy Ground ... The Miracle

of Caring for Children at Life's End

I am a pediatric palliative care nurse. I care for the smallest and most vulnerable and those who love them. Every day I am reminded that what we do matters, it shapes our humanity and brings meaning and miracle to our lives. Caring for children at life's end is sacred work. They tiptoe into our lives at their most vulnerable. They capture our hearts with beautiful, brave smiles that shine through the hurt. The shadow of life-limiting illness does not dim their light. Each moment in their presence can be viewed as miraculous, reminding us that we work on holy ground as we stand in awe and marvel at their quiet courage and strength. Tenderly, with great care, we walk alongside, promising to gentle the journey as life ebbs. We companion them to the edges of their lifetimes, traveling as far as we can go. They live and laugh and love and leave our world forever changed. Sometimes their memories slip out of our eyes and softly roll down our cheeks. Our hearts are heavy, they are grace-full.

We are the last responders. While first responders race in to save lives, last responders stand steadfast at bedsides to gentle life's end. Many cannot imagine choosing to shoulder the burden of this work. We come to the realization that we can't always cure, but we can always care, and find healing in that. As last responders, we gentle the end-of-life journey, anticipating and managing symptoms, guiding and supporting medical decision-making. We help families make memories and create legacy to sustain them through their grief. Last responders come to know on a deep soul level, that the arc of each lifetime is precious and perfect, no matter how short or how long.

Our healing presence is itself a quiet miracle, a promise to each child and family that we will be both a guiding light, and a solid touchstone upon which to lean, as time fades from weeks to days to hours. The sacred work of caring for children with terminal illness is a paradox: We are powerful witnesses to great love and great loss, which is at once draining and fulfilling in almost the same breath. It helps me to allow the suffering we see to nudge us toward thinking about what really matters ... Presence, kindness, forgiveness, grace, and love. In this way, we allow for miracles ... Perhaps not the big, flashy miracle that is cure, but rather the smaller, sweeter miracles that seek no attention.

Nursing presence is one such miracle. It is the miraculous inner strength into which we tap to stand in the fire with our patients and not shrink back. I stand vigil with my small brave charge. I manage pain and symptoms. I hold up her grieving parents with quiet reassurances: "You have left no stone unturned ... She is loved beyond measure." I lean over and whisper into her small ear, "You can rest, little friend. I will watch over your parents." A soft sigh escapes, a furrow in a little brow relaxes, and a last breath is taken. She has earned her wings. Here are a couple of grace-full pages from her beautiful little life story:

Once upon a time, there was an angel in training ...

She was the only five-year-old I know who has ever asked for a harp from Make-a-wish Foundation. According to her parents, her heart's desire was to be able to "play like the angels." She received her harp. Her parents told us that the first song she wanted to learn to play was *Amazing Grace*. She learned it quickly — I would venture to guess that she knew her time was precious (a wise old soul indeed!). And though her parents were holding back the tears, they told me these things with a kind of miraculous awe and the hope that comes with great faith. What a gift she gave them. I am comforted by the thought that she knew the path on which she was supposed to be walking. She knew, in some place deep in her soul, that her truth to share on this journey was one of faith and amazing grace. A week before we scanned her, this little one was already telling her parents that her tumor was back. She began to prepare them for her loss from this earthly world, while reassuring them of her place of comfort in the heavens. "I'll always be with you," she promised her mom and dad.

At the tender age of five, she softly laid her harp down for the last time, but held on long enough for her grandparents to arrive from across the country, knowing that her parents would need the support. Amazing Grace, how sweet the sound! Not The End...

These brave young souls, this holy ground upon which we practice this healing tradition we call nursing; creates sacred space. Sometimes it is achingly sacred as we reflect on lifetimes and nursing presence and miracles ... Sometimes I write to soothe the ache and bring light to the darkness:

Let the beauty
We love
Be what we do.
There are hundreds
Of ways to kneel and
Kiss the ground.
RUMI

A Grace-Full Heart

The fine fight has been fought,
The faith has been kept,
The vigil is done.
The moment is sacred as the soul leaves,
On the delicate whisper of an angel's wings.
I lean into its light; graced by a fleeting glimpse
  of what lies Beyond.
I pray for peace, for wisdom to find gentle words of
  comfort and solace.
A teardrop escapes, more sweet than bitter,
Leaving a glistening trail in its wake;
Softly falling, I watch it turn into a fragile shooting star.
My heart is heavy; it is Grace-full.
I am a powerful witness to a sacred lifetime.
The miracle has happened; it has been my privilege.

Caring for children at life's end is sacred work, and the place we stand in any given moment is holy ground. We are grateful witness to miracles born of tender loving care. They give us solace and strength and help us bear the seemingly unbearable.
We kiss the ground ...

JoAnne Auger

Rita's Miracle

Rita R. Romito-DiGiacomo BS, BSN, RN, PCCN,
North Olmsted, Ohio, USA

This story is about two experiences relating to my father who
experienced many medical issues and challenges that he always
faced with strength, courage, and a strong will to live. He survived
multiple myeloma, open heart surgery, kidney failure, right leg
amputation, ruptured bowel with a colostomy, vision loss in one eye,
non-healing wounds, and many other medical issues, spanning more
than a decade. I want to focus on the last year of his life.

It was winter and my father's fistula had developed a clot, I took
him to the large hospital that had done the initial surgery. The
vascular doctor who was caring for my father attempted to repair
his fistula, and during the procedure my father suffered a grand
mal seizure and was rushed to the ICU. In time, the team became
concerned about his lab values and decided to attempt dialysis. After
several failed attempts and significant blood loss, they stopped. That
day, I arrived to visit my father, and I was not aware of what had
transpired. I noticed that he was very pale and not making sense
when he spoke. He also complained of severe abdominal pain for
which they gave pain medication. I was very nervous and expressed
concern to the nurse manager of the ICU, ironically I had gone to
nursing school with him and he was working that evening. I told him
that something was very wrong and that I was worried about my
father. I didn't want my father to be alone that evening, so my brother
stayed with him since I had to go to work in the morning. That night
they moved my father from the ICU to a regular floor; it was around
midnight when I received a call from my brother who was very upset.
My brother stated that as he was watching my father, he noticed

that my father was breathing more slowly, and then just stopped breathing. He notified the nurse right away, and they called a code blue. I immediately got dressed and made my way downtown.

There was a horrible snowstorm that night so I could only drive very slowly; it was the longest drive of my life. I remember crying and praying the entire way, asking God to please not let him die. When I arrived at the hospital, my father was intubated and back in the ICU. The doctors told us that my father experienced pulseless electrical activity and that he probably would not survive. My father received multiple blood transfusions, was on continuous dialysis, and suffered complications during his stay in the ICU. One day, his vascular doctor happened to stop in to see him and the look on his face said it all. He stated that my father was very, very sick, reinforcing the fear that he may not survive.

Over time, and to the surprise of many, my father improved enough that he was able to breathe on his own. He was off of the IV medications, and continuous dialysis was stopped. Eventually, he was transferred to a regular floor where he remained until his discharge. When that day finally came, my father had been bed bound for a month and was very edematous, fluid weeping from his arms. He was discharged to the rehabilitation facility that he was very familiar with, which brought us some comfort. My father also had several consecutive dialysis sessions to remove all of the excess fluid.

After being in rehab for only a couple of weeks, and working with the amazing therapist that helped him after his amputation, my father was standing again. Around this time, I took my father to his follow up appointment with his vascular doctor. I remember when I wheeled my father into the office, and he stood on one leg to be weighed, the vascular doctor was at the front desk area and when he saw my father standing on one leg, his jaw dropped. When we got into an exam room the doctor came in, sat down in front of my father, held his hand and just looked at him for a moment, then he quietly repeated, you are very special. The doctor, like many of us, was amazed at my father's recovery.

My father had come close to death many times over the years, but the last year of his life was the most difficult with the amputation, and then two months later suffering a ruptured bowel. It was a miracle that he survived a condition that people half his age often do not, but with his strength and many prayers, he did. Back at the rehab facility they referred to my father as a cat with nine lives. He had such a strong will to live, and I always attributed his amazing recoveries to this inner strength as well as the grace of God. My father's experiences and recoveries were to me miracles and true mysteries of a world beyond ours.

About one year had passed when my father would fight his last battle. During his last year of life, my father was home only about four weeks, the remainder of the time he was either in the hospital or the rehabilitation facility. It was Christmas Eve and I had my parents over for dinner. I was grateful that we were able to be together for the holiday since my mother was in a rehabilitation facility due to a recent fall at home. Fortunately, the facility allowed the visit. After dinner, my mother was brought back to the rehab facility, and I brought my father home. I stayed with him that night and my brother would arrive the next day to help with his care. Sometime during the night, my father became very short of breath so I called for an ambulance. When we arrived at the hospital, my father was put on BiPAP to help him breathe, and over several days he was given many antibiotics, but nothing was working. During this time my father went through a period of agitation and confusion.

One day, when my family and I were at his bedside, he became very alert, appeared very upset and yelled out that my niece Julia was in an accident and we had to help her.

We tried to calm him down and told him that she was fine, but his fear persisted and the look in his eyes was as if he just witnessed the crash. My niece was notified of his condition and came in to see my father. She states that when he looked at her, it was as if he could not believe that she was there and okay. My family and I thought it was probably ICU psychosis, which he had experienced before.

As time passed, my father became more agitated but lucid, at that point he clearly stated his wishes to us; he was ready to go. As difficult as it was to hear, and with no hope of recovery, we honored his wishes. The doctors removed all equipment, and my father was made comfortable. He was transferred to a regular room and later that day he passed away peacefully. I recall the sky and clouds being a brilliant orange when he passed away, and I knew in my heart that he was okay and no longer suffering.

Six months later, almost to the day, my niece Julia was a passenger in a car with four of her friends, one being her best friend. They were involved in a horrible accident and the car was totaled. All four of Julia's friends did not survive the crash, she was the only survivor. Julia's father, my brother, was soon to celebrate his birthday and he received the greatest gift of all, his daughter survived a horrific car accident. I remember my brother calling me from the hospital in the early morning and I immediately got dressed and drove to the hospital. We were talking with the nurse in the waiting area, and my brother and I were recalling how we lost our father just six months earlier. Then, we both looked at each other and with quivering voices recalled my father saying that Julia was in an accident. Could it have been a premonition or vision of what was to come?

The morning of the second day that Julia was in the hospital my brother went in to see her. He recalled that she was sleeping and he sat in the chair next to her. When Julia awoke, she stretched and looked at the chair that my brother was sitting in and asked where Papa went. Julia told my brother that she had a dream that my father was sitting in that very chair and he told her that she needs to get better and that Grandma was worried about her. Two weeks later, Julia could not recall that dream.

It was a miracle that Julia survived such a horrific crash with only minor injuries. Our family believes in our hearts that my father had a vision of the crash prior to his death, that he protected Julia the night of the crash, and then visited her during her recovery. To me this truly is an example of the mysteries and miracles that can occur, and that can change our lives forever.

Rita R. Romito-DiGiacomo

Katy's Miracle

Katy Fisher-Cunningham MSN, RN, Oklahoma City, Oklahoma, USA

My work as a floor nurse involved caring primarily for neuroscience patients. Due to the nature of the patients' conditions and comorbidities, many of them would experience auditory and or visual hallucinations. The hallucinations varied from benign to bizarre. One shift I was assigned to care for a patient I will never forget. From report I learned he was a male in his late seventies on palliative care and not expected to survive the shift. As I entered the room to introduce myself to the patient and his family, I could tell they were having a difficult time. Tearful family members hovered near the bedside of a frail, combative gentleman. The air was thick with the smell of lemon glycerin mouth swabs and menthol. The patient was restless and moaned softly as he stirred in his bed. As I placed my fingertips on his arm to alert him of my presence, he turned his head toward me with a blank expression. His eyes were bright in contrast against his lined faced.

I began my work collecting the patient's shift vitals, conducting a focused assessment, and establishing a plan of care for the day with the patient's family which mainly included keeping him comfortable. Throughout the morning the patient continued to look restless, so I administered medications for pain and sedation. About thirty minutes before the patient passed, he became exceptionally calm and started talking in a whisper so faint that it was barely audible. His family members remained at his bedside and leaned down, placing their faces close to his to discern what he was saying. As I approached him, I realized he was having an in-depth conversation with his mother. The patient looked up at me with tears brimming in his eyes and stated clearly, "My Mom is here. Mom is calling me home. She's my angel." At that point, everyone in the room, including myself, became emotional.

That is what he believed because it is what he heard and what he saw. It was truly miraculous. I was thrilled to see his family was supportive of the patient. No one discouraged him or attempted to reorient him. They spoke to him softly and even encouraged him to follow his mother, his angel. I was happy to support them in that decision because that was what the patient needed for his care. I also truly believed that she was with him in that moment. That was what he needed to relax, to let go, to be released from pain and fear. Some people may think "Oh, it's just a hallucination," but to this patient and his family that was an angel coming to take him home. It was such an intimate and special experience. I feel privileged that as his nurse I was able to be present and observe the experience of peace, love, and comfort at the end of what is not always the smoothest transition. The environment was completely welcoming and inviting to the possibilities of miracles. It was a miraculous event and during the experience I could not help but think, "Jean Watson would love this."

Katy Fisher-Cunningham

Nicole's Miracle

Nicole Brodrick RN, DNP, PMHNP-BC, Boulder, Colorado, USA

It was April 14th, 2016. My mom had called from Las Vegas telling me that she had just transferred my father to a hospice facility. He had suffered a stroke in January and had not recovered. I knew from the urgency of her call that I needed to get to see him that day. I was able to get on a flight that next day and got to the hospice facility around 2pm. I had been in a hospice facility once before, but this time it was different as I was more aware of my surroundings. I walked in and the room had sunlight beaming in through the big windows, so much so, that I had to squint to see my mom who was sitting by the window with my dad's cousin. I walked directly to my dad who lay eyes closed and still in his hospital bed. My mom had prepped me so I knew what to expect – my dad was on 6 L of oxygen and having the Cheyne-Stokes restorations. He had been non communicative since he had been transferred to hospice. As I approached him I went into my nursing mode since I saw that he needed oral care badly from his dry cracked lips and caked white tongue which people get from extensive mouth breathing. I wet some swabs and cleaned his mouth ... When I was done, I leaned over and kissed my dad and told him, "Dad, I love you." He then said to me, "I love you too." I looked at him, but his eyes were still closed. I asked my mom and his cousin if they heard him say that to me. They had not. I know I did not imagine it.

At that moment a wave of peace fell over me and the room seemed a little brighter. We stayed with him until about 3pm and then went to get something to eat near the facility. We returned an hour later. He took his last breath around 5pm that night. The experience was surreal as I was amazed as to how much peace I felt that day. I had that space open to allow for miracles and it had happened. I believe he was waiting for me to see him until he felt he could move onto the next existence. Thank you for letting me share my experience.

Nicole Brodrick

Robert's Miracle

Robert Reynoso MSN/Ed, RN, CEN, Henderson, Nevada, USA

I was leading my Fundamentals clinical group (the first of four semesters) on the very last shift of the semester. I pride myself on discussing the Caritas processes with my groups. They are well-versed to correspond the processes to the more technical and clinical aspects of the profession. Caritas process #10 is tough, but so obvious in many ways. Let me share my story.

I was rounding on the group near our departure time. I was aware of the patient from what I heard in report. She was dying and Do-Not-Resuscitate was in place. No students were assigned to the room, but I always encourage them to answer lights and help as needed. As I walked by the room, I noted my student (a twenty-year-old), seeming a bit more overwhelmed than usual, and so I turned into the room. The student was trying to obtain vital signs. She was doing the best she could, falling back on technical knowledge to help. Years of experience told me that this patient was in her final hours.

The attending RN was doing her best, but the demands of the medical-surgical shift were obvious and she was very busy. The daughter had just left and the patient was alone. I did have a plan for departure and discussion, but I felt that this had occurred for a reason. After discussing with the RN, we received permission to stay with the patient. I had no idea how long it would be but I committed the students, at least for some time, to make her last moments as comfortable as possible. At this point, she was not lucid and was sleeping with diminishing respirations.

I turned down the fluorescent lights and we took seats around her. We found some lovely music on the television. We held her hand. We stroked her hair. We shared our most beautiful stories of the beautiful places in the world. We were there. About one hour later, she passed in front of the eight of us. While I give a Death and Dying lesson in lecture, this woman gave my students (and one cranky old ER nurse) a beautiful lesson I could not surpass. My students (nicknamed: Guardians of the Galaxy) made me so proud, and this miracle will no doubt make them better nurses, citizens, and humans. I gave my students the option to not sit with her, but they all made it clear that they wanted to take part. All of my lessons and demonstrations of care and compassion synced perfectly and for a moment, we were all fully equals in the provision of human care and kindness. In many ways, I was expecting a typical day today, and to move on, but this gift manifested itself upon our world. We were and are grateful.

Robert Reynoso

Shandra's
Miracle

Shandra Kight RN, BSN, CPN, Caritas Coach,
Aurora, Colorado, USA

It's Sunday June 24th, the sun is gently rising over the mountains on a calm and seemingly peaceful summer morning. I'm trying to sleep, so tired and worn out. Feeling defeated and exhausted, the kind of exhaustion that is starting to settle into my bones. My alarm hasn't sounded yet and I just want a few more minutes of peace. However, sleep evades me, something keeps stirring inside me, telling me to get up until I finally decide enough fighting and grab my phone to see what time it is.

I have multiple messages and missed calls from the hospital. I recognize this number because it is the hospital my mom has been a patient in for the past five days. Dozens of tests have been completed with days' and days' worth of a medical work up but still no clear answer or plan. All the while I have slowly watched my mom's health continue to deteriorate. I am now suddenly wide awake, angry at myself for putting the phone on silent because I so selfishly wanted to get some rest. I press play on the message, my heart starting to race and my anxiety rising. As the message plays I hear a scared voice, quiet but quick to the point, struggling to get the words out. I knew the voice well, it was my mom's bedside nurse, "Shandra, you need to give me a call as soon as possible, it's regarding your mom. Please call me as soon as you get this." I dial the number and she answers.

"Shandra ... your mother has coded." These are words I never thought my ears would hear, words I never thought would be spoken to me about someone I love so deeply. Words that will alter the course of not only my mother's humanity, but mine as well. Not expecting, not anticipating this, the journey I would be traveling. That is the road I was about to take ... the one we would be taking together.

Helpless, seemingly hopeless, and recklessly out of control. A downward spiraling started in this moment, a rapid unraveling of all I knew, a shaking into the depths of my soul.

"Shandra your mother had an aneurysm in her brain that ruptured and she is bleeding into her brain." More words I never thought possible, words I couldn't fathom. I remember trying to make a plan for the things I needed to say, struggling to find the words, to be brave. Then walking into the ICU room, seeing a pale, close to death human figure swallowed up by the big hospital bed. Tubes surrounding her, machines keeping her alive, serving their purpose bringing life to the lifeless.

Holding a hand that couldn't hold mine back. I felt it ... a pulse ... beating ... Her heart is working on its own even if barely clinging to life. Standing together all of us holding hands, family, loved ones, those miles away on speaker phone. Saying goodbye, speaking words of love, releasing her to God, to the universe but never forgetting. Asking her to take care of herself for the first time in her life, to do what she needs to do. Even though every fiber in my body screams at me and all I want to say is just hold on, just fight, just come back to me ... I still need you. Hoping love will overcome, surrounding her with love, not being able to say enough words to show the depth of my love for her. Suffering in love, loving her enough to say goodbye ... Watching as they take her away from me, in flight by helicopter so she can be saved, letting go of her hand ... One more kiss, one more exclamation of love. Away she flies beyond my reach, beyond my control, past my focus, I'm left shaking, praying and hoping that love is enough ... Praying for a miracle.

From that moment, Mom stayed in a Neurological ICU for over thirty days on life support. During her stay, she remained one of the most challenging and complex patients on the unit. Many more times over I was told the expectation she would survive was low and if she did make it no one could tell me if and when she would wake up. From the ICU she went to a long-term acute care center for a month where again she had multiple complications but was able to get off of the ventilator and she started to wake up. She then went to a rehabilitation facility for two months making just enough progress for insurance to deny any further coverage just a few days before I graduated from CCEP. We were able to transition Mom to assisted living for the next transition of care where subsequently her appendix ruptured requiring emergency surgery which again the odds were not in her favor.

On the week of January 9th 2019, Mom had her follow up angiogram with the neurosurgeon to check on the condition of the aneurysm. What was once a twisted dangerous tangle of blood vessels has now straightened out and flows well like a gently bending river. When the surgeon came to review the procedure and obtain consent Mom was joking with him, completely herself, quick and full of wit. The only way you would even know something may have happened to her is by watching her slower gait and reliance on a walker to move around.

On January 18th 2019, Mom walked through the front door of her home, somewhere she hadn't been for seven months. She is now home independently regaining control over her health and her life. Despite all the odds she made it home with a quality of life better now than it was before. She is my mom fully present and every day taking another step on the path of healing. She is a living miracle.

Shandra Kight

Roberta's

Miracles

Roberta Christopher EdD, MSN, APRN, NE-BC, CHTS-CP,
Jacksonville, Florida, USA

Bread Crumbs & Nine Lives

Roberta's Miracle 1:

My life started pre-conceptually as a miracle. My young, eighteen-year-old single mother sensed that she was pregnant. In those days, pregnancy tests were not as reliable as they are today. The pregnancy tests she took continued to report false negatives. My mother was on the precipice of a choice in her life. The choice, however, depended on a positive pregnancy test. My mother never received the positive pregnancy test. All tests reported negative. As the months passed, it was apparent that she was pregnant and that I was moving inside of her. The choice had been made – One of my nine lives.

My younger years were filled with emotional and physical child abuse, uncertainty, and poverty. Despite these shortcomings, I always knew that a presence was with me and guiding my life. I call this presence God. I have vivid memories of sitting near a lake during a Girl Scouts camping trip and having such a sense of wonder and knowing. I trusted this knowing, even as a child.

One week before my high school graduation, a male friend and I were about to leave my home to go to my grandmother's, a few miles down the road. My younger brother wanted to ride with us. Something in the deepest pit of my soul screamed out that he was not meant to go. It made no logical sense to me at the time. I asked myself, "Why can't he go with us?" Nevertheless, I was compelled to follow this bread crumb, and so I asked if my brother could come later with my other family members. I hopped in the truck and sat closely by my male companion. I always, always wear my seat belt. However, this one time I did not and reasoned that it was just a few miles. What could happen?

The road to my grandmother's house was loose gravel. The driver was not accustomed to driving on these types of roads. About a mile away from my grandmother's house, we hit a loose pile of gravel. The driver lost control of the truck. The truck crashed into a ditch bank and flipped repeatedly and came to rest upside down. Interestingly, as the truck began to crash, I felt a strong sense of peace and safety. From a rational perspective, I should have first slammed into the rearview mirror and then have been ejected through the windshield, at the least. The seat where my brother would have sat was completely crushed into the truck. He would not have survived. The driver was upside down and his leg was trapped in the damage. I, however, was sitting upright in a small space that sufficed. Not a scratch on me and no injuries.

Roberta's Miracle 2:

As the truck wheels began climbing up the pile of gravel along the ditch bank, I felt that my time had come. In slow motion I said a prayer, not to spare my life but rather to spare the driver's life. I was at peace and knew good things were to come. Like a gust of wind, I was propelled outside of the truck and found myself looking down from above. I sensed a presence with me while I watched the event unfold. I saw the truck flipping, flipping, and flipping. I could hear all the crashing sounds and witnessed the dust spiraling in vivid detail. I felt safe and at peace while still praying for the driver. I had resolved that I was about to go to heaven and was being allowed to see the driver make it out safely. As fast as I left the truck, swoosh – I was back in the truck looking at the upside-down driver. I sat there briefly puzzled. I was back and my life had been spared. The slowed time began to accelerate, and I again felt connected to the present moment. I was able to loosen the driver's leg and we crawled out through an opening. The driver was beat up but recovered. I walked away with curiosity and a sense of knowing a miracle had occurred that could not be explained by conventional science. The miracle had cemented that I had a divine purpose in this life and the bread crumbs were with intention.

Roberta's Miracle 3:

The bread crumbs have continued throughout my life, and I have remained open and curious to see where they would lead me next. On September 10, 2017, my family and I were watching the approach of hurricane Irma on the television. We lived along the St. John's River and had prepared accordingly. We were in a zone that had just been requested to evacuate. South Florida had been essentially emptied out and there were no hotels in Florida, Georgia, Alabama, or South Carolina available. Local shelters had been opened, but you must bring crates for your animals. We had two dogs and two cats. Despite rational thinking and bread crumbs, we stayed and closely observed the path of the storm. Irma made a shift away from Miami toward the west coast of Florida. The projected impact at that moment was to be similar to or less than the hurricane from the previous year. We still had power and were fully stocked for several days. All the furniture was raised, just in case. We decided to watchfully wait. The river had risen but seemed to have stabilized. My husband and daughter went to bed. Having worked in a large academic trauma center, I was glued to the television in emergency preparedness mode. I retired to my bedroom to continue the watchful waiting there.

An emergency preparedness text from the County command center began screaming from my phone. I went to jump up and the power went off. I hung my feet off the bed and stepped into about a foot of water. Flash flood means flash flood! The water had breached our readied house in a matter of minutes. Had the power not gone off at that instant, I would have been electrocuted. Again, my life had been spared. Life Number Three by my count. I grabbed the flashlight and woke the family. The two dogs and two cats were all on our bed – This never happens! We grabbed our animals and go bags to head out the door. About that time another alert went off. This alert was different and stated a tornado was imminent. My daughter and I looked at each other intensely, as if to say, "What are we going to do now?!" I glanced at my phone and noted the alert was from Jacksonville University, where I worked as faculty. My poor students and colleagues were about to be hit by a tornado! I snapped back to my own peril and began swimming with the dogs to my vehicle that was staged on higher ground. My husband got the cats to his truck. There was no light and the water was to our waist as we entered the vehicles. My emergency preparedness mind went to Plan B. We could potentially make it to a neighbor's house, which had a second floor. To our amazement, the road on the higher elevation was not yet fully covered. We literally drove for our lives and made it to the nearby bridge and safety.

As a researcher, I could try to explain these events in my life through deductive reasoning. I know in the core of my being and soul that deductive reasoning would not be sufficient in explaining the sense of knowing and calling (e.g. the bread crumbs), or the countless miracles (e.g. three lives to date that I am aware of); that bring me to this writing. Rather, my openness to the mystery of life, spirituality, and the many unknowns provide me with a foundation of wonder and a childlike sense of curiosity. As such, my heart remains authentically open during the caring process to miracles, despite what scientific evidence may be indicating. Further, this centered knowing propels me to live a purpose-driven life filled with openness, intention, love, peace, and JOY! Follow your bread crumbs ...

Roberta Christopher

Beverley's Miracle

Beverley Lugo RN, MSN, Caritas Coach, Boise, Idaho, USA

My first Caritas Coach weekend was shortly after I was ordained as an Episcopal minister. It was a really happy time for me because I had achieved something that I was called to do as a child, but I never thought was possible for a woman, especially a divorced woman. I'd been a nurse in critical care, hospice and nursing education for more than fifteen years. Becoming a minister was not about leaving the nursing profession but rather, about being open to a spiritual call which allowed me to integrate my deeply held spiritual beliefs with the sacred role of a nurse. It was also a way for me to provide healing outside the physical realm in the parish setting.

By Sunday night of the Caritas Coach weekend I was pretty worn out from all the learning and social interaction, and I just wanted the final "Caring through Art" session to be done. In task-oriented mode, I wanted to check it off and go home. The session started out with centering and group sharing, and then the facilitator had us dip a piece of twine into black tempera paint, and then draw something on a blank piece of paper.

I entered into the experience with skepticism. I can't draw, paint, or sculpt. To an introvert like me, at the end of the busy weekend, this activity seemed annoying. But I quietly balled my piece of twine up and dropped it in the black paint and then pulled it out and put it in the middle of my blank white paper and spread out the ends across the page until most of the paper had some black lines on it. While the paper and ink dried, the facilitator had us search through magazines for pictures that represented the essence of caring for a group collage. As people chatted and flipped through the magazines, quickly tearing out images and gluing them on a long piece of butcher paper, I sat by myself and took my time.

I could have torn out the first image I found, of a sunrise or a baby, but I wanted my part of the collage to represent the core of my caring. I had enjoyed hearing different perspectives about chakras, centering, and meditation throughout the weekend. In the midst of it all I'd been reflecting over the course of the weekend about my own beliefs, which formed the moral and philosophical framework for my human caring literacy. It seemed sad to me that American Christianity has evolved into something so antithetical to its roots in the one I believe to be the perfect source of love and caring, a Jewish rabbi named Jesus who died to communicate in the flesh, that there is a Universal Source of love available and present for us all.

So, I searched until I found this photograph in a travel magazine of a bare-chested African woman with a giant cross necklace dangling between her breasts. I was the last person to glue my image that represented caring to the paper, everyone else was already using the chalk to color in their black tempera painted lines, chatting about how unartistic they were with the people around them.

There were only a few pieces of chalk left by the time I got to the table with my paper with its thoughtlessly applied dried black lines. I hastily grabbed them and stood in front of my paper, resolved to put some color on the page and wrap up the assignment. But then, from my task-driven mode of being, I looked down onto the paper to see the outline of a woman. It was an abstract image of a woman, but a woman nonetheless. It was a woman that I could not have drawn on my own and she was beautiful.

She was just there, without any artistic effort or ability, an unintentional abstract Renaissance work of art. It was unexplainable and transcendent. I smiled and as I began to add color to the woman's outline, I experienced a moment of pure joy. I thought about how I put away my childhood dreams of being a minister when my marriage ended. I never could have imagined that I – this imperfect woman by the world's standards could ever be a good enough. I heard the Holy Spirit speaking to me from within, "See who you are. You are my Beloved daughter and I called you. Out of the chaos and confusion of your life, a beautiful woman has emerged." It was a sacred moment and I started to laugh. I began to think about Caritas Process #10 which invites an "opening to allowance for mysteries, miracles, and a higher, deeper order of life's phenomena that cannot be understood with the ordinary mind and mind-set" (Watson, 2008, p. 193). I shared the image and the sacred experience of creating it with my group members and then carefully tucked it into the bottom of my suitcase for the flight home that night.

My artwork made it home intact despite the chaos of dirty clothes and shoes which shared space in my luggage in the overhead bin of an airplane. I spent a fortune framing it and it hangs on the wall in my bedroom reminding me to be open to mystery, synchronicity, and to work with the Spirit within me. It reminds me that good things come out of chaos and confusion for those who are willing to open themselves up to divine possibilities. And, it reminds me to share this healing hope in both of the noble and sacred calls of my life.

Watson, J. (2008). *Nursing: The philosophy and science of caring* (Revised edn). Boulder, CO: University Press of Colorado.

Beverley Lugo

Beverley Lugo
Divine Possibilities

Section IV

Debby's Miracle

Debby Flickinger RN, PhD, Concord, California, USA

The Watson Effect: **The Emergence of Miracles in a Living System**

I knew from the time I was a child that I wanted to be a teacher. When I was nine years old, I had a doll called Suzy Smart. She had a blackboard, a little desk, and a chair. Suzy talked when you pulled the string on her back. I gathered the children in my neighborhood, and we would sit in a circle and I would use Suzy's blackboard to teach spelling and arithmetic. After the passing of my mother when I was fifteen, I was forced from this path to pursue careers that would support me financially and I moved away from my dream.

Years later, laid off, and at home one day watching *The View*, something clicked for me when I heard Barbara Walters ask the panel, "If you only had twenty years, what would you do with them?" I was thinking, "Wow, I surely do have twenty more years, at the very least ..." In that moment, I realized I had been given a miracle. I would pick myself up and start a new journey.

Before this miracle entered my life, twenty years seemed like an endless time to suffer through until retirement rolled around. I knew in that moment that those twenty years would be the beginning to a whole new life, and possibly the career of my dreams. It was simple: Spirit had shown me an opportunity, one I had put aside and dreaded, in a whole new light. Through a single television show I saw my path before me: I had to go back to school in order to follow my path of teaching, and suddenly my purpose seemed attainable.

Following my heart, I started taking classes at a local community college. One class led to another and another. Suddenly, and miraculously I might add, I found myself in the Transformative Studies doctoral program at the California Institute of Integral Studies. Never in my wildest dreams did I imagine that I would be Dr. Debby Flickinger.

Several years into the program, my daughter approached me about a certification that might enhance my doctoral work in transformative studies and consciousness. Dr. Jean Watson's *Caritas Principles* (2008) spoke directly to my soul. The word Caritas, Latin for cherish (Watson, 2008, p. 39), gave me a feeling of optimism and hope that had been missing in my academic studies previously. More than anything else, Principle #10 felt to me as though it had been with me all of my life. Seeing in print, "Open to mystery and allow miracles to enter" (Watson, 2008, p. 40) was an awakening, or cosmic "aha moment," and in that moment, the trajectory of my life and work transformed.

I saw Caritas Principle #10 as a lens in which to reflect deeply, not only on my current way of thinking about things, but on my childhood and teenage years. I had been left on my own, facing unknown challenges in a complex world, and with a feeling of despair and abandonment. I now know that it was allowing miracles to come into my life, and to flow with the river that would lead me to the here and now. I search for something bigger than me; I allow the mysteries of the unknown to enter in, and I stay open to possibility in whatever shape it might take.

I am a creative and motivated individual, dedicated to environmental developments such as community building; fostering a sustainable future and leading to social and economic improvements. I actively learn and grow nurturing community relationships that contribute to social and environmental health. I see my knowledge, engagement, challenges, and transformations, as just the beginning. Even now, a never-ending flame burns in my heart continuously seeking a divine transpersonal advancement of my mind, body, and spirit. Principle #10 aligned in me, not only the awareness of miracles, but the heart and soul of my life's path – to work with children.

As my studies moved forward, I became certain that my research would be about middle-schoolers and sustainability. My goal was to develop an afterschool curriculum that would essentially get children out of the classroom and into the trees. I wanted them to make a connection to the earth in a way that is not possible without getting outside and experiencing nature at its best. As I worked on this, I realized that the one element missing from the academics of sustainability was caring. Although Caring Science is designed for nurses, it made perfect sense to me to carry it into another academic discipline, sustainability, that seemingly lacked a deeper and more personal connection to the earth and nature (Watson, 2008, Louve, 2008).

Most people want to take care of the earth, but not as many people make the connection between science and spirit. The potential impact of Caring Science and Caring Theory, especially Principle #10 and its focus on being open to miracles, began to bubble up from depths of my soul and infused itself into everything I read, wrote, or thought. I sat with the Principle, I meditated on it, and I dreamed it. My own consciousness was becoming more and more heart-centered (Watson, 2008). The words Caring Sustainability™ were like a wellspring that pushed up through my body like a geyser, to reshape and transform my doctoral dissertation. Caring Sustainability™ became my original contribution, and the force behind my desire to take Jean Watson's work to an expanded audience.

As I continued to explore Dr. Watson's books, it was evident that the original Caritas principles were deepening and evolving as a living system into something even more profound. They had become not just principles, but processes. Principle #10 became Process #10 and has since evolved into "Open to spiritual, existential, mysterious; allow for miracles" (Watson, 2018, p. 140). The fluidity of Dr. Watson's work as a living system was, for me, another miracle. I saw that education is a living system, and things are constantly changing as new information and understanding come our way. It's as though the web of life (Capra, 1996) can tear and be rewoven in a way that can redirect our course and deepen our understanding of how the universe works and the role we, as individuals, play in creating our own reality.

For me, sustainability has been infused with caring, and the future of my work no longer seeks to separate these concepts. The Watson Effect emerged as a web, linking the aspect of caring to virtually everything that was covered. The Watson Effect permeated the study with mindfulness, caring, and created a model for caring sustainability. As my understanding of the Caring Sustainability™ concept and the Watson Effect deepened, I found it was reflected in other aspects of my work.

Throughout the course of writing this personal narrative, my relationship to Process #10 has heightened my awareness, and expanded my consciousness. "This energy is nearly visible in the air around us. It is as though we give off light" (Watson, 2018, p. 141). Today, I am much more aware of this. I am often embraced by a swirl of energy that fills me with loving kindness, and that tells me, that I too, am loved. Through Process #10, "Open to spiritual, existential, mysterious; allow for miracles" (Watson, 2018, p. 140), my conscious being is elevated to new heights. I am wholly connected to the web of the universe and the divine Spirit.

Several years ago, I began a creative process that allowed me to randomly write down words and phrases and feed them into a computer application called WordArt. This simple process provided me with a complex, visual perspective of my work. At first the process was totally random, but later, as you can see in the example below, I found myself giving it more shape, which changed the perspective of both my thoughts and feelings. WordArt has provided a way for me to visualize more deeply the meaning of my work, and my writing.

I am a woman, a mother, a grandmother, a feminist, and
an activist. I believe that the spiritual journey of every being is
to explore the divine relationship of the self to the higher self
(Bynum, 2012; Chopra, 2014; Sitzman & Watson, 2014; Smith,
2016; Wilber, 2006). In this context, the higher self is our total soul
consciousness. When individuals enter in to a harmonious alliance
with the universe, they can view the world with an enriching sense
of hope and inspiration. Most children have a thirst for knowledge
which reaches beyond reading, writing, and arithmetic; yet few
have exposure to transpersonal concepts, sustainability, or outdoor
activities. As a result, they are disconnected from the self, from their
environment, and from their community.

When I immerse myself in words and knowledge, I find that
I inevitably come full circle. What started as playing teacher in
my backyard with Suzy Smart and a handful of kids from the
neighborhood, had led me back to wanting to make a difference

in the lives of others, through teaching. I knew that my work would involve numerous people and that I needed to take it to the community and beyond. As Capra (1996) stated, "The more we study the major problems of our time, the more we come to realize that they cannot be understood in isolation. They are systemic problems, which means that they are interconnected and interdependent" (p. 3). I have come to believe in the infiniteness of possibility.

Since I began this work, miracles have continued to happen. I was hired to teach a course at Union Institute University (UIU) based in Cincinnati, Ohio. This opportunity allowed me to bring Caring Science and Caring Theory to a course that examines Education, Social Justice, and Sustainability. Furthermore, the outreach to an unexpected community demonstrates how wide-reaching and powerful the Caritas processes can be, and makes one wonder if they can't be introduced into other academic disciplines such as political science, communications, and business, as well as the arts and humanities. Taking it further, what if the Caritas processes infused the lives of our children throughout their educational journeys? What if the processes were passed down generation to generation? Watson (2008) suggests that, "If one holds higher-thought consciousness, the entire [energy] field can be, and is being, repatterned by the [human] consciousness" (p. 140). Can you imagine the miracle that would shift and change the consciousness of the planet?

I don't have all the answers and I am open to the discovery of new practices and techniques to ensure a better sense of all I am learning every day of my life. I have been graced with a road map for a deeper exploration into the creation of an afterschool program teaching Caring Sustainability™. For that I am forever grateful to have had the opportunity to explore sustainability through the lens of the Caritas principles and Caring Science, especially Process #10.

I am convinced that the experiential holistic activities of gratitude, forgiveness, and appreciation of self, others, as well as Mother Earth will have a lasting impact on these young hearts. Through teaching the core concepts of Caring Science with a holistic approach in an after-school program the children will be touched in life-changing, life-giving ways. Loving kindness will, I trust, cause the children to transcend as conscious beings to a higher level of understanding as they move from childhood into adulthood (Sitzman &Watson, 2017).

I am certain that this exploration into and through Caritas process #10 has just begun for me. As my journey continues, my own web of life expands, and I look forward to new horizons. The Watson Effect has had a tremendous impact on the way I walk in the world. It has infused itself into the essence of all I teach, all I write, and all I do for my community. Process #10, "Open to spiritual, existential, mysterious; allow for miracles" (Watson, 2018, p. 140) will be my guide as I move forward in this dance we call life. In closing, I offer up to my teachers, my ancestors, future generations, my family, extended family, and ultimately to Spirit, the words of Brian Swimme (1996):

The consciousness that learns it is at the origin point of the universe is itself an origin point of the universe. The awareness that bubbles up each moment that we identify as ourselves is rooted in the originating activity of the universe. We are all of us arising together at the center of the cosmos. (p. 112)

Debby Flickinger

Flickinger References

Bynum, E. B. (2012). *Dark light consciousness: Melanin serpent power and the luminous matrix of reality.* Rochester, VT: Inner Traditions.

Capra, F. (1996). *The web of life: A new scientific understanding of living systems.* New York, NY: Anchor Books.

Chopra, D. (2014, December 18). *The future of God* [Video file]. Retrieved from https://www.youtube.com/watch?v=91RCukg5BGo

Louve, R. (2009). Children and nature: The great disconnect. In L. Buzzell & C. Chalquist (Eds.), *Ecotherapy: Healing with nature in mind* (pp. 205 – 10). San Francisco, CA: Sierra Club Books.

Sitzman, K., & Watson, J. (2014). *Caring science, mindful practice: Implementing Watson's human caring theory.* New York, NY: Springer.

Sitzman, K., & Watson, J. (2017). *Watson's caring in the digital world: A guide for caring when interacting, teaching, and learning in cyberspace.* New York, NY: Springer.

Smith, J. K. A. (2016). *You are what you love: The spiritual power of habit.* Grand Rapids, MI: Brazos Press.

Swimme, B. T. (1996). *The hidden heart of the cosmos: Humanity and the new story.* Maryknoll, New York, NY: Orbis Books.

Watson, J. (2008). *Nursing: The philosophy and science of caring* (Rev. edn.). Boulder, CO: University Press of Colorado.

Watson, J. (2018). *Unitary caring science: The philosophy and praxis of nursing.* Boulder, CO: University Press of Colorado. doi:10.5876/9781607327561

Wilber, K. (2006). Integral spirituality: A startling new role for religion in the modern and postmodern world. Boston, MA: Integral Books.

Word Art [Computer Software]. (n.d). Retrieved from https://www.wordart.com/

Watson Caring Science Institute

About Watson Caring Science Institute

Watson Caring Science Institute is an international non-profit 501C(3) organization that advances the unitary philosophies, theories and practices of 'Caring Science', developed by Dr. Jean Watson. Caring Science is a transdisciplinary approach that incorporates the art and science of nursing and includes concepts from the fields of philosophy, ethics, ecology and mind-body-spirit medicine.

There are an estimated 400 hospitals throughout the USA, in which their professional practice model is based upon Watson's philosophy and theory of human caring science. The institute has trained over 500 Caritas Coaches® globally to translate caring science theory into concrete human-to-human practices that help to repattern the culture of healthcare, whereby the practitioners 'live out' the theory in their professional and personal lives.

Focusing on research, education, practice, and leadership, Watson Caring Science Institute aims to deepen the development and understanding of Caring Science and Caritas Practices®, to dramatically transform patient/family experiences of caring and healing in schools, hospitals, the wider community and our planet.

LOTUS
LIBRARY

About Lotus Library

Lotus Library is a publication imprint of Watson Caring Science Institute. Following from the philosophy of Caring Science, Lotus Library aims to encompass and showcase a humanitarian, human science orientation to human caring processes, phenomena and experiences. Our mission is rooted in compassionate care and healing of the mind-body-spirit as one. Our publications exemplify a transdisciplinary approach to sustaining caring/healing as a global covenant with humanity/Mother Earth. Lotus Library provides a forum for nurses and others to give voice to phenomena which otherwise may be ignored or dismissed, celebrating the mysteries of life, death suffering and joy, embracing the miracles of existence.

About Jean Watson

Dr. Jean Watson is Distinguished Professor and Dean Emerita, University of Colorado Denver, College of Nursing Anschutz Medical Center campus, where she held the nation's first endowed Chair in Caring Science for 16 years. She is founder of the original Center for Human Caring in Colorado and is a Fellow of the American Academy of Nursing; past President of the National League for Nursing; founding member of International Association in Human Caring and International Caritas Consortium. She is Founder and Director of the non-profit foundation, Watson Caring Science Institute (www.watsoncaringscience.org). In 2013 Dr. Watson was inducted as a Living Legend by the American Academy of Nursing, its highest honor. Her global work has resulted in her being awarded 15 Honorary Doctoral Degrees, 12, international.

As author/co-author of over 30 books on caring, her latest books range from empirical measurements and international research on caring, to new postmodern philosophies of caring and healing, philosophy and science of caring and unitary caring science as sacred science, global advance in caring literacy. Her books have received the American Journal of Nursing's "Book of the Year" award and seek to bridge paradigms as well as point toward transformative models, now, and the future.

For further Lotus Library reading visit our online store:
www.watsoncaringscience.org/the-caring-store/

CPSIA information can be obtained
at www.ICGtesting.com
Printed in the USA
FSHW010130051119

9 781733 123211